BONISA
A CHILD OF AFRICA

And other sheep I have, which are not of this fold;
them also I must bring, and they shall hear my voice;
and there shall be one flock, and one Shepherd.

John 10:16

Dutch Editions:
First published in 1964
Second edition in 1965
Third edition in 1968
Forth edition in 1978
Fifth edition in 1982
Sixth edition in 1996

Bonisa, a child of Africa
Mrs. M.A. Mijnders - Van Woerden
© De Lichtkring, Schoolstraat 17, 2161 HB LISSE, The Netherlands - 2001
Production: B.V. Uitgeverij de Banier, Utrecht
Translation: Ronella
Illustrations: Adri Burghout
ISBN 90 806193 1 0

Bonisa
A child of Africa

Based on the original by
Mrs. M.A. Mijnders-van Woerden.

Translated from Dutch by Ronella
and edited by the author.

INTRODUCTION

European and African Missionaries...,
You, who took us to far away kraals and huts,
in your vast forests;
You, who led us through the jungle, in the dark night
where mysterious forest sounds of wild animals
could be heard in the wilderness;
You, who on a moonlit night, brought us to the edge
of the great Shandingu river
and to the kraal of the chief at Limpo-Lupanda.
We give to you all our heartfelt thanks for this token of friendship.
It is through your help that we could gather
detailed information to write the story of
Bonisa, a child in dark Africa.

African friends,

We say to you all a hearty thanks for your hospitality;
that we could sit in your family circle by the fire;
and listen to your stories
about the forest life of your people;
Jhula and Amos, who interpreted;
Tshebo and Roger, who took us early in the morning
into the awakening forest,
where the tropical birds sang their morning song;
where impala, zebra, kudu and giraffes
quenched their thirst at the river in the first morning light;
you, who showed us the honey guide and the honey tree
and the wonders of God's creation,
in Africa's nature...;
your friendship we will not forget.

But..., young, black friends in Africa,
girls and boys from South, East, West,
and Central Africa;
It is the expression in your dark, restless,
searching children's eyes...,
that we took back with us out of your great land
as an unforgettable memory;
Your eyes which mirrored fear
as the dusk came down over the forests;
your fear of the spirits...;
you, who wandered about as sheep without a shepherd.

M. A. Mijnders van Woerden

1. WHERE ARE THE SHEEP?

Quick as a flash, Bonisa runs along the narrow forest trail of red sand. Every now and then she stands still, panting; puts her fingers in her mouth, and makes a shrill, whistling sound that penetrates far into the quiet forest.

Ahead of her and far behind her in the wood, she hears the bleating of the sheep and goats that she must bring back to their kraal. The bleating of the animals is an answer to her whistle call.

Oh, those naughty animals! Unexpectedly, a big stick had been thrown, and landed right in the middle of the flock. They were frightened and had fled into different directions.

She knew quite well, who threw that piece of wood at them; it came out of the cornfield of Nkube. Nkube is the neighbour who lives in a nearby kraal. He is probably afraid that her sheep and goats will come into his cornfield and eat the corn plants and sugarcane. Now she will have to worry about gathering the whole flock again, and take them to the kraal before it is dark.

The sheep and goats that ran ahead of her will probably find their way back to the kraal, but she will have to turn back to find the animals that went the wrong way.

Bonisa turns around and runs, as fast as she can, back down the trail. Her black arms swing alongside her skinny body as she runs swiftly along the path, making the red sand fly up all around her.

Ah, there... She sees some sheep grazing peacefully in the wood, browsing on the leaves of a low-hanging branch. With one leap she leaves the forest trail and runs, barefoot, through the bushes toward the sheep. "Go on home," she calls angrily, as she hits the animals several times on their backs with the thin stick in her hand.

The sheep are startled. They jump nervously around the juicy leaves of the tree they had just found, and run along. The sheep are driven on as the stick constantly taps them on the back if they go in the wrong direction.

The girl runs after them, bending quickly and easily, crawling under the low-hanging branches. She jumps over small thorn bushes and scrapes her legs on the sharp thorns, but pretends not to feel it. She has to make sure that the flock will be home soon, because dusk is rapidly settling over the forest.

She suddenly hears a voice: "Ah... Bonisa. Why don't you take better care of the sheep? I have a few of them here among my herd of cattle. They were at the foot of the hill on the way to the valley, but I drove them along with my herd."

The girl stands still, wipes the sweat from her brow with her hand, and tries to pull the dry leaves and twigs out of her hair. "Ah, Tukula," she says, somewhat surprised to see the young African, who is coming towards her with a herd of red cows and oxen.

Tukula stands still right in front of her, looks at her angrily and says: "Bonisa... you are only little; you can't even take good care of the sheep. It is almost dark and the sheep and goats are wandering alone in the forest. Tonight the hyenas and jackals will tear them apart."

"No, that's not true. I always take good care of the flock. Every evening I make it to the kraal before dusk, with all the animals, but... but Nkube was in his cornfield, he shouted to the sheep and threw a branch into the flock. Then they fled in every direction," Bonisa defends herself, "I couldn't help it at all!"

Tukula is the eldest son of the chief over all the kraals in the Lupanda valley. He has the biggest herd of beautiful red cattle, with such long, sharp horns that they could throw a leopard into the air in just a few seconds, and kill it.

For a moment Tukula lets his hand rest heavily on Bonisa's shoulder and continues looking at her angrily while he asks: "When you come home, and some of the sheep are missing, what will your father say then?"

Bonisa's dark eyes stare at him in fright as she says shyly: "I'm

8

not allowed to come home if any of the sheep are missing."

"Now then, you might as well stay in the forest tonight, because I saw another three sheep in the valley. You can't bring them into the kraal before dark."

She shivers at the thought that on this dark night she will not sleep inside the hut, but will have to wander through the forest to find the sheep.

The herd of cattle has come closer. They gather around Tukula. Some of the animals lick his hand and the great, old ox rubs his head on Tukula's shoulder.

The young man puts his arm around the animal's neck and strokes its head while he speaks to the child. "Go home, Bonisa," he says again sternly, "and make sure that from now on you keep the flock together. You will have to leave the sheep in the valley because it's getting too dark to find them now."

Tukula drives his animals to the path that leads higher up into the hills, and glances back quickly at the little, black girl who runs through the forest and whistles to gather the sheep and goats together.

The last glow of red golden light from the setting sun disappears behind the forest, as Bonisa drives her flock into the enclosure beside the kraal. It is late tonight. The animals are already becoming wary and restless; they only feel comfortable in the dark, when they are safely in their enclosure for the night.

As she closes the gate, she looks once more over the sheep that are now peacefully chewing the cud and standing close together inside the enclosure. She searches among the woolly, moving animals to find out which sheep are missing. Most of the animals are completely white, but her favourite sheep has a black head with a white stripe between its eyes. The stripe on its head is narrow, and gets wider towards its mouth. She calls it 'Blacky'; Blacky is always close to her!

In the afternoon, when the forest has become very hot, Bonisa lies down with the flock in the shadow of the Tshabella trees. Then Blacky is always close beside her with its head on her arm.

Sometimes she sleeps for such a long time that she does not notice that the flock is already grazing again, and has started walking in the direction of the Bembasiriver to drink. They become thirsty, because the sun burns bright and hot on the African savanna. Then Blacky wakes her up, licks with its tongue over her face and bleats softly.

Instantly, Bonisa awakes then and goes along with the flock, over the hills; they all run very quickly but Blacky always stays close beside her. She loves this sheep very much.

Tensely and fearfully, she begins to search for Blacky among the moving animals. But she does not see it. The entire flock is made up of sixty-two sheep and goats, of which twelve animals have a black head. On each animal, the black spots are different. Bonisa knows the sheep and goats very well, but she does not see Blacky among the flock! She bends, crawls quickly under the gate of the enclosure, and searches desperately among the sheep. "Blacky," she calls anxiously. "Blacky, where are you?"

The sheep bleat in response, but no Blacky comes toward her to lay its head in her hands and lick her arm.

Bonisa feels miserable. She leans against the rough fencing, made of wooden poles, while again her eyes search in the last, faint golden glow of light from the setting sun, to see which other sheep are not there.

Two more sheep are missing from the flock; one lamb with black front legs, and a bigger sheep with one black ear. Bonisa knows her goats and sheep very well. Never has one of them run away; every evening she is home before dark, and the whole flock is in the kraal on time.

She grips the fence tightly, and leans her small head against a pole; she is very sad. She wants to cry, but that is not allowed.

Only babies who are hungry do that. When you are big enough to herd the sheep in the forest, you are not allowed to cry any more!

"Alaah, Bonisa, you're late tonight with the sheep," announces the gleeful voice of a boy behind her. It is Nkwee, an older brother of 14 years, who takes care of the cattle that belong to their father. Nkwee has just checked the fence of the ox pen to make sure the animals cannot break out during the night, by pushing the gate open with their horns. There are two stubborn oxen in the herd that keep trying to break out. They know that close by, in neighbour Nkube's cornfield, they can find really good corn and sugarcane.

Bonisa doesn't answer; she stands there silent, leaning against the gate with her hands clenched around a pole.

"Ah, you can't talk?" asks Nkwee, and pulls playfully on her black hair. But when she still doesn't say anything, he notices that something isn't right.

He walks to the gate of the enclosure, jumps over it with an agile leap, and stands beside his sister in the sheep kraal. "You aren't hungry?" he asks "Why don't you go to the kraal, where the cooking pots are?"

"Three sheep are still in the woods" she answers, her heart sinking "Two of them belonging to father, and my beautiful Blackhead."

Nkwee becomes angry. He clenches his fists in front of her face. "Does father already know about this?"

"No, I don't dare to go into the kraal."

"Stay here; I will go and tell."

Nkwee leaves, jumps over the gate of the sheep's pen, and walks hurriedly into the kraal, where the women are busy preparing the evening meal.

"Oooohji..." the boy calls as he stops, still out of breath. "Bonisa has lost three sheep; they are still in the woods!"

A couple of women, who are squatted on the ground, mixing the

12

cornmeal and water for the evening meal, stand up immediately and call out in shock: "Oooohji... three sheep wandered off, oooohji."

From the biggest hut in the center of the kraal, a tall, strong man appears and walks toward the shocked family. The women and children move away, to give him more room to talk with Nkwee. Beside the fire he stands still and looks at the boy with ominous, threatening eyes. "Speak, Nkwee," he says sharply.

The boy waits for a moment, while the women and children gather in a semi circle behind Nkwee, so that they will not miss any of the conversation. "The sheep are in the kraal now, but there is a sad message. Three sheep are missing, still roaming around in the woods; Bonisa is too small, she can't take care of the sheep by herself."

After giving these unhappy tidings to his father, Nkwee takes one step backward and stands motionless. The women also carefully take a few steps backwards, although it is hardly noticeable in the dim light. The little children feel the silent tension and press closely together.

It seems as if Vundla, the father of Bonisa and head of the family in this kraal, suddenly appears even bigger than he already is. He raises his head high; his eyes flicker in anger. "Go and call Bonisa" he commands Nkwee "and you, Sikla, bring me the whip from my hut!"

Quiet murmuring starts among the women. A thin woman with a baby strapped on her back slowly takes several steps forward. Her head is bent as she makes a deep bow in front of the angry man. Then she stands up again, but stays hunched over in front of him. "Vundla, do not punish my child; she is still young. I will go into the forest and look for the animals, and before the sun comes up, I will be back with the sheep," she says softly.

"Why don't *you* make sure that more corn and wheat can be taken from your field" the man says roughly "Bonisa will look for the sheep herself and bring them home."

Silently Sikla slips out of the hut, gives the whip to his father, and steals away to the outer edge of the kraal, as if he is scared that he will be punished too. Again it is quiet in the kraal... very quiet... The dry branches crackle in the fire. Red flames lick up high along the black earthen pot in which corncobs are cooking over the fire.

Then Nkwee comes through the opening of the kraal enclosure. He walks slowly, with boldness. Behind him, small and scared, comes Bonisa. She feels the silence in the kraal. All the women and children are looking at her. At a few steps distance from her father she makes a bow and crouches to the ground.

"How do you dare to come into the kraal while three sheep are still missing?" the angry man yells at Bonisa.

She stands up before she answers. "I did not dare to come into the kraal, so I stayed with the sheep in the night pen, but then Nkwee came to get me," she says softly.

"You didn't think, did you, that you could sleep in the hut tonight?" the raging man shouts. She does not answer, but stands waiting, her head bent.

Vundla waves the whip up and down right in front of Bonisa, to frighten her. The whip cracks through the horrible silence in the kraal.

"Tomorrow" he yells "Tomorrow, I will beat you with this whip if you dare to come back without the sheep. What good are children who can't look after my flock?" He commands Bonisa to accompany him to the 'spirit tree'.

She follows her father, small and frightened, while he cracks the whip up and down.

The most important place in the kraal is the kraalhead's hut. His hut is built beside a great Tshabela tree, from which heavy, widely spreadout branches grow. Vundla says that in this Tshabela tree

14

live the spirits of the ancestors, who protect the family.

When something happens in the kraal, the spirits will see it. When something is spoken, the spirits will hear it, and when they are not satisfied with the honour they receive, they will cause misfortune and accidents to take place in the kraal.

Chief Vundla worships and prays to the spirits with much devotion this evening. He stops in front of the spirit tree. Bonisa must stand beside him. The women and children have followed them and stand at some distance, trembling with fear.

It is quiet in the kraal. A strange, dark silence can be sensed beneath the spirit tree. The awesome silence of the African forests, where only the chirping of the crickets foretells the coming of the night.

Vundla makes a deep bow underneath the Tshabela tree, and asks: "Amadhlozi, protect us and let us find our sheep. Make the spirits of our enemies powerless. We will honour you for this. Make our family strong and courageous to kill the enemies, and may our spirit one day come into your spirit world to receive a place of honour."

The man grows silent for some time, while Bonisa clenches her small hands into fists; she is afraid! She waits for the punishment that will be brought upon her.

Her father begins to speak again, with a heavy voice, while he holds his hand over Bonisa's head. "Amadhlozi, look down with scorn on this child of our family. She did not bring the flock safely into our kraal before it became dark, under your protection. Many enemy spirits roam around at night in the woods; they may kill our sheep. This child is guilty. She will go into the woods and look for the sheep. Protect the sheep from the evil spirits, so that they will come home safely. Then we will make a feast and bring a sacrifice to honour you."

Bonisa makes a bow under the Tshabela tree and carefully looks up at the thick leafy canopy that rustles in the evening wind. A shock goes through her when suddenly she sees that above the treetop, redgolden lights appear and dance up and down over her head.

"Oooohji..." the women call, as they see the little lights.

That is a good sign. The spirits are sending a group of fireflies to show the way with their nightly magic. The fireflies twirl around the spirit tree, then suddenly shoot forward to the center of the kraal. They flutter around and then fly on again toward the opening of the kraal enclosure.

"Ah..." the women call excitedly... "Quick Bonisa, follow the lights that the amadhlozi have sent; they will send you in the right direction."

Bonisa's dark eyes follow the lights, which are dancing up and down. She runs through the kraal exit and follows the fireflies into the night that is becoming darker and darker.

In the kraal, the women go back to the cooking pots. They put more branches on the fire and stir the corn porridge. The children are sitting on the ground, pressed tightly together and whisper softly to each other.

Sikla has been keeping a close eye on his father to see when he must take the whip back to the hut.

But father Vundla is squatting down at the entrance of his hut, muttering sombre words, restlessly bouncing the whip up and down. He doesn't look at his wives and children. He is thinking about all the misfortune he has had in his kraal.

Porcupines had been in the peanut fields. They had turned up the soil and ripped out the peanut plants. The baboons from the woods had come into his fields, screeching happily, while stealing many nuts. The little boys of Vundla's kraal had tried to scare them away with sticks and by making much noise, but the naughty animals had come back time and again.

The corn has not grown well this year either. The stalks are thin and the corncobs too small. Two cows had died after an evil spirit had made them sick. Ah... the spirits of the ancestors need to be worshiped even more, then everything will become better and there will be no more misfortune!

Vundla is in deep thought. He doesn't even notice that MaMoyo, his oldest wife, is squatting in front of him a small distance away; in her hand she holds out a boiled corn cob for him. He is thinking about Bonisa, who came home without three of his beautiful sheep. Ah... when she returns from the forest without the sheep, he will whip her! He lost three beautiful sheep, while he still has to pay three cows as a dowry for Bonisa's mother.

Vundla's thoughts become even more sombre.

When he married MaWanda, Bonisa's mother, he had to pay seven cows as a dowry to her father. He only had four cows and he promised to pay the other three after a few years. Now there have already been eleven corn harvests since MaWanda came into his kraal, and still the three cows have not yet been sent to MaWanda's father.

When this corn harvest is passed, MaWanda's father will come, far from the North, from the other side of the great Shandingu-river. He will ask for the three cows, or another payment. This is the law of the tribe. After twelve years the dowry has to be paid, and if not...

Vundla sighs deeply... then, MaWanda's father will take one of his daughters, as payment.

The excited barking of the dogs, as they hear the eerie laughter of hyenas in the distance, disturbs Vundla's thoughts. He looks up and sees MaMoyo sitting in front of him with the corncob. Ah, that's good, he would like one of those!

As he nods to his wife that he would like to have the corncob, she stands up. She peels away the sheath of the cob, and puts the warm, cooked corncob in his hands. She has chosen the best and the biggest one for him. Then she returns to the fire, to the pot with thick corn porridge, to give her children their evening meal. In the small group of children, a cheerful atmosphere has returned.

Sethu, the dog, is sleeping peacefully against a hut, until a hen pecks at a tick in his ear. Maybe Sethu is thinking in his dreams that it is a wild animal from the forest. He jumps up and barks angrily at the hen that runs away, cackling with fright. Sethu is right behind it. In his anger he is not watching where he is going and bumps into MaWanda, who is sitting at her little fire.

Ah, MaWanda falls over and the baby on her back rolls with her on the ground. She has a little pot with corn porridge and that falls too. The mixture runs out of the pot over the red sand.

Two piglets come along, oinking with glee, and slurp up the mixture from the ground, and a goat licks the pot clean.

MaWanda looks around sheepishly; all her evening food has disappeared!

MaMoyo has rolled out her straw sleeping mat beside her fire. She kneels down on the mat and scoops up large portions of thick corn porridge out of the big, black pot into a basket.

Four girls and five boys squat around the same basket. They take a small portion of the stiff porridge with their right hand, form it into a ball and dip it into a pot of cooked, wild vegetables. It tastes very good.

But there is no meat. They have not tasted meat for a long time. Father Vundla will have to go hunting again to catch an antelope or a wild boar.

The children are talking happily, and making plans for the new day, in which they hope to catch birds in the forest. Nkwee and Sikla will make a bow, and the birds they catch will be roasted over a fire, while the cattle are resting in the heat of the afternoon, in the shadow of the trees.

Bonisa's mother, MaWanda, has walked toward her hut with unsteady steps. Devastated, she seats herself on the ground. She tries to calm the crying baby, by giving him some sour milk from a small gourd that she has in her hut. Fortunately, the baby becomes quiet.

MaWanda has noticed how the children and the other wives of Vundla had laughed at her when she fell over. Ah, it scares her to know that she is so weak and tired. When she has to get water from the river, she fills the gourd only half-full. The other women must not be allowed to notice this. She can no longer carry a big calabash filled with ten liters of water on her head. She can also hardly carry the heavy loads of reedgrass and wood. Sometimes she thinks she is going to die.

But she is not allowed to die yet! First, she must work hard because there are still three cows to be paid. If she dies before the dowry is paid off, then her spirit will not stay with the ancestors of this kraal, but will float as a lone spirit through the wilderness; so she thinks.

She searches in the hut for the piece of sugarcane that Bonisa had brought home the other day, and breaks off a piece. She chews it up between her teeth, and takes the sweet marrow from her mouth to feed the baby. The child sucks at it eagerly and then falls asleep.

MaWanda stays up for a long time with the sleeping boy in her lap; her thoughts are gloomy. Where would Bonisa be now? On other nights, Bonisa would help her prepare the meal and take care of her brother, while she swept the kraal for the night. Now she feels lonely and fears for her child, who will spend the night alone in the forest without protection.

Her thoughts are interrupted by Vundla's strong voice; he is calling her name.

MaWanda already understands why; - she has to go and help the other women sweep the red sand in the kraal.

Carefully she lets the sleeping baby slide from her back and takes with her a big, leafy branch from her hut and walks toward the kraal entrance.

The other women also bring a branch and begin to sweep, each one in her own section of the kraal. They start at the fence and with strong strokes sweep back and forth over the red sand. They walk backwards as they sweep so the red ground in front of them stays even. All the footprints of the day are being swept away.

On the morning of the new day, Vundla will be the first one to get out of the hut. Then he will be able to see by the evenly swept ground whether there are any footprints of people or animals imprinted in the red sand. When there are tracks of a leopard, he goes hunting to catch the animal.

Sometimes there are tracks of snakes, other animals or people. This is how the people in the kraal know what dangers threaten them at night.

MaMoyo and the two other wives of Vundla have finished sweeping and have returned to their own huts, but MaWanda is still busy. Her weak body trembles and her breathing is rapid and shallow as she moves the branch across the kraal ground. She feels sick as she sweeps and shuffles slowly backwards until she reaches the opening to her hut.

For a moment, she looks across the silent kraal to the far away darkness where the faint light of the moon begins to light up the black forest. There, far away, is her child, Bonisa.

2. NIGHT IN THE FOREST

With intense effort, Bonisa follows the fireflies over the narrow trail. The path winds through the forest and leads up to the higher peaks of the Lupanda hills.

As she runs past Nkube's kraal, the flickering lights suddenly disappear. A new fear grips her. Why doesn't she see the lights of the fireflies anymore? And why just as she passes behind the kraal of Nkube, her enemy? Nkube, who had spooked the sheep today, making them wander far off, after he had thrown a piece of wood in the midst of the flock.

She gazes sharply into the darkness before her, desperately searching for the dancing redgolden lights. Would the spirits of her ancestors not want to help her anymore? Ah... there are of course the powerful evil spirits in the kraal of Nkube that have killed the lights of the fire flies. Oh... then they would want to kill her too!

She wants to flee, far away from the dangerous spirits in the kraal of Nkube. She runs along again; the trail leads higher and higher, to the highest hilltop. She is getting so tired, but she cannot stand still to rest. She wants to go on to get as far away as possible from those evil spirits.

Higher up on the hill she suddenly stops. An obscure creature scurries right in front of her on the trail; it's a porcupine with long sharp quills. It disappears among the bushes. Then it is very quiet again... A dark, tense silence.

Bonisa looks around; where should she go? The night has just begun, and it will be long. Where are her sheep? Where should she look?

Wherever she looks, are trees with branches thickly covered with leaves. And in those trees are the spirits. All those evil spirits are staring at her as if they want to destroy her.

She must go on. Haunted by fear, she follows the path to the highest hilltop. Breathing heavily, she stands still, trembling with loneliness in this great, dark wilderness.

Bonisa is still young, but she is a child of the forest, and having grown up in the wilderness, she knows the sounds of the forest. She knows which forest creatures have found their shelter for the night after this hot day. The antelopes, impala, mountain goats and black buffaloes have disappeared into the thick woods in the dim evening light, but they are not dangerous and won't bring her any harm.

After the sun has gone down, and the dim light turns into darkness, the African forest grows silent for some time. The tall straight trunks of the great forest trees stand like innumerable black forms, unmoving, in the vast forest. Among the tall trunks, grow dense bushes and fern plants, making it impossible to see what is hiding underneath. There are the dens of the aardvarks, which are anteaters, with their long snouts, and of the mamba snakes and the bush cats.

Above her head, a branch begins to move. It creaks; a dark figure steals across the swaying branch. Suddenly a loud cry comes from one of the trees. It cuts through the silence of the night, and is followed by terrible cries from other trees. They come from the baboons that call each other to begin their nightly journeys through the treetops.

The male baboon, the leader of the group, that had given the first signal, right above Bonisa's head, now swings down to the ground and jumps right in front of the shocked girl. He walks around her, examining her.

She stands unmoved; maybe the baboon won't hurt her.

The animal doesn't think the girl is important enough to look at for very long. He runs back to the tree, and with great speed, swings himself into the high branches.

Then a loud screeching begins. The apes chase each other, swinging from one tree to the next, then the entire group disappears to the lower part of the forest. Again, there is a strange calm over the forest.

Bonisa presses her hands together in fright, and waits for more noises from the wilderness. An owl flies silently past her, close to the ground, hunting for lizards and rats. The branches of the low bushes begin to move and rustle. The snapping sounds of dead branches breaking on the forest floor, make her even more afraid. Everywhere in the woods, different movements begin.

Nocturnal creatures, which have left their dens in search of prey, make mysterious sounds as they stir about through the woods. She hears the sounds, but she cannot see the animals. The strange laughing of hyenas deep in the woods sends shivers through Bonisa's body.

Immediately after that follows the sinister crying of the jackals and wild dogs; the sound is coming from all directions. Now the fear inside the black child becomes too much to bear. The hyenas and the wild dogs are coming; those dangerous enemies that every inhabitant of the forest is afraid of; those vicious wild animals that search in the night after prey; to kill and to tear apart. But, where can she go?

Bonisa, a child of the forest, believes there is no hope for her. The angry spirits of the enemies glare at her from all sides. An immeasurable wilderness of darkness and threatening dangers surrounds her.

In despair, she sinks to the forest ground, hunched over and frozen with fear, her head bent. Bonisa is crying in misery and loneliness...

The moonlight begins to shine over the Lupanda valley. On one of the hilltops stands a strong, young man. He peers with a sharp hunter's gaze over the river that winds its way through the deep valley.

Before him, halfway down the hill, lies the large kraal that belongs to his father and family. The small groups of huts lie

together in a dreamlike rest under the moonlit, African night.

The young African stands hidden in the shadow of a Baobab tree, and glances once more over the kraal, where the wood fires are still smoldering, even after the women and children have gone into the huts to sleep.

The young man is Tukula, the eldest son of chief Sitemba. Tukula has been standing there for a long time. He stands on guard. He wants to know who the enemy is that sneaks past the kraal every night, and who has made his father so sick.

On this evening, when the women and children were sitting around the fires for the corn meal, Tukula had sat with his father.

Sitemba was lying sick in his hut, and he was afraid. He told his eldest son that at night the pain in his back is worse than during the day. The pain is especially bad in the nights when the moon is dead, and when the darkness lingers. There must be an enemy in the area surrounding the kraal! At night, the enemy sends an evil spirit with special powers, and bites him in the back with sharp teeth. Chief Sitemba knows when he has been bewitched.

Several weeks ago, when he was coming home from the hunt, hot and sweaty, taking the long way home through the forest to his kraal, the evil spirit came out of the woods and bit him in his chest.

He felt at once that something had touched him. Cold shivers went through his body. A searing pain in his back proved the presence of the evil spirit.

For several weeks, Sitemba has been lying sick in his hut. He lies on his sleeping mat, very close to the fire, but he shakes and shivers, and in the night, the teeth of the evil spirit bite sharply into his back. He feels tightness in his chest and he can barely breathe. In his eyes, there is a dull expression of fear.

Tukula must stand on guard tonight, just on this night when the moon is coming alive again. He must look carefully to discover the skulking enemy.

Tukula's glance is attracted to something dark that slowly moves forward over the grass in the moonlight, along the river. It must be a big eland. Every so often, the animal turns its head nervously from left to right. It raises its head high; the beautiful horns stand out in the moonlight; its ears are wide open to hear every sound.

Then it stands completely still for a moment. It stands there, a dark silhouette, etched against the light reflected in the river. The fiendish laughter of a troop of hyenas suddenly rips through the peaceful silence of the Lupanda valley. The eland shoots forward like an arrow across the grassy plain.

Tukula's glance intensely follows the terrified antelope, until the animal disappears in the high grass that grows on the Lupanda hills.

Would the animal still be able to reach its herd in the forest, in time to be able to defend itself along with the entire group? Together in the forest the antelope can form a ring in which they all put their heads down, pointing their sharp horns forward to ward off the attack of predators. When an antelope is attacked alone, it has no chance of survival.

Tukula cannot see the hyenas at this distance but he does hear their excited cries. And far beyond sounds the howling of the jackals, which always follow the hyenas, to devour the remainder of the prey.

A few more times he sees the head of the eland show above the elephant grass while disappearing in its flight. The animal has now almost reached the edge of the forest. Once more, its head is visible above the yellow reedgrasss as it takes another great leap.

Tukula stares after it and waits for the sounds that will give away the attack of the hyenas. It remains quiet. The eland may now have reached the forest on the hills...

Then, a scream is heard in the distance. A cry that makes Tukula shiver. That sound does not belong to the antelope. That is not the sound of an animal. It is the anguished scream of a human being.

Ah... Tukula trembles with emotion. Is this the voice of the enemy that creeps through the valley to make his father sick? But the enemy always comes without a sound, and would not betray itself by calling out. Then, to whom does the voice belong?

For a long time, he remains standing in the shadow of the Baobab tree. Just as still as the trunk of the tree. For hours, he stands there, watching and listening.

Tukula did not sleep very long that night. At the first shimmer of daylight he leaves his hut and takes the path to the Lupanda hills. He wants to know to whom the voice belonged, that came from the forest last night. Maybe he can find the footprints. He remembers very well the place where the antelope left the elephant grass and went into the woods.

At the downtrodden reedgrasss, he stops. The cloven hoofs of the antelope have left a clear imprint on the soft ground. He follows the tracks over the path to the top of the hills. The animal had taken big leaps because the hoof marks are printed deeply and widely apart into the earth.

"Ah..." he mumbles, and stares at the ground. There are marks imprinted in the red earth. Tukula bends down to the ground. "Ah..." he says again. His own foot is now beside the footprints. "Ah... they belong to a child." Would these tracks go together with the scream that he heard last night?

He walks several meters forward where the small footprints are imprinted somewhat more clearly; there are also footprints of baboons. The tracks of the antelope here disappear off the path and into the woods. Some freshly broken branches point to the direction in which the antelope disappeared.

Tukula squats down, and carefully studies the imprint on the ground. A child was here and had sat on the ground. He sees the marks of hands and fingers pressed into the earth. Then he stands up again and follows the tracks where the little feet went.

The footprints follow the trail and go down into the valley. The child must have walked quickly; the distance between the footprints is great. Where the elephant grass stops, the trail makes a bend to the left through the grassy field and toward the riverbed. The footprints end there.

Rather quickly, he finds another track, going up, cutting straight through the elephantgrasss. Finally, after a tiresome search in the forest, he finds the footprints again clearly imprinted on the sandy ground of an old vacated kraal. He follows the tracks to a deserted hut on the backside of the kraal, where they disappear into the entrance of the hut. There are no footprints on the ground coming back out of the hut, so someone must still be inside.

Tukula stops a moment, coughs to warn that someone is coming. There is no answer. He squats in the doorway and peers into the dark space. He hears nothing.

After several minutes he enters the old hut, squats in the center of it and looks around with searching eyes. Slowly his eyes get used to the dim light and he is able to see what is inside. An empty space with a few piles of firewood.

He walks through the hut, examines the tiedup branches and moves them out of the way. A soft moaning comes from behind the firewood. He carefully lifts up the branches and sees a small dark figure lying on the ground, pressed against the wall. Tukula bends over and kneels on the ground.

Two large, dark, fearful eyes of a child stare back at him. He takes the little black hands into his and asks: "Who are you?"

The child begins to cry and sob. "My sheep... my sheep got away."

"Ah," he answers, "You are Bonisa. How did you get here?"

Still shaking because of everything she has gone through, she sits up straight against the wall of the hut and tells what happened during the past night. How her father had sent her into the woods to find the sheep, and that the lights of the good spirits were killed behind the kraal of Nkube. Her fear of all the dark and evil spirits

28

that followed her.

Then Tukula tells her that in the night, when the moon came to life with its light shining over the valley, he had seen an antelope fleeing into the forest. Then a terrifying scream had come from the woods on the Lupanda hills. Whose scream was that?

Bonisa shivers, she begins to cry again and can hardly tell the rest.

"You are cold Bonisa; I will make a fire to warm you," says Tukula. He takes a dry stick and spins it back and fore, very fast, inside the hole of a wooden fire-block into which he has first put a handful of dry grass. While spinning the stick quickly between his hands, the dry grass begins to smoke and soon there is a little flame. He puts it on the ground in the center of the hut and covers it with thin branches. In a few minutes, a fire flickers.

Bonisa crawls to the red flames and soon feels the warm glow of the fire against her body. She remains huddled shyly as she goes on with her story: Last night when she had sat on the ground, because she didn't know where to go, an antelope had suddenly come up the hill with wild bounds. He had jumped right past her with his heavy hooves. Terrified she had screamed, but there was no one to help her.

She had fled further, first down the hill and then into the valley. After that, she had gone again into the woods to find shelter, until in the moonlight she spotted some old rundown huts. There were no sleeping mats or cowhides inside, on which she could sleep. There were only some branches for firewood. She crawled in behind them so that perhaps the evil spirits would not find her and would pass by the hut. She had fallen asleep until Tukula found her.

Now that Bonisa has told everything, it is quiet again in the hut. She feels the warm glow of the fire penetrate through her whole body. It feels nice; she doesn't shiver so much anymore.

She looks at Tukula who is sitting on the other side of the fire, staring into the flames. "Ah..." Bonisa says "when I'm bigger and I have my own cornfield, then I will take the biggest cobs, in a basket on my head, to the kraal of Tukula, as a gift, because he found me and made a fire to warm me."

For a moment a broad smile shows on Tukula's face, but then he asks: "If Bonisa returns to Vundla's kraal without the sheep, what will happen?"

Bonisa is shocked. "The sheep, I have to find them. On this new day I will find them and bring them back to the kraal. My father will be happy, and he will drink beer."

"Are you hungry?" Tukula asks.

Bonisa nods. "Yes, I'm very hungry."

"Stay here by the fire and wait until I come back. When I return here, I will have some sugarcane and a cob of corn for you," says Tukula.

"Did the amadhlozi send Tukula to this hut to find me?" asks the child. The young man stands beside the fire and remains quiet for a long time. Bonisa stares at him in deep reverence and says: "The amadhlozi can also give me back my sheep."

Then he looks at the child, sitting in front of him on the ground beside the fire, and answers: "The amadhlozi are powerful, but there is another one. He is the strongest. He is King over all the spirits." Then he turns around and leaves the hut.

3. THE NEW MORNING

Bonisa is walking through the waking forest on the Lupanda hills. With quick steps she follows Tukula, the son of the chief. In the hut she had eaten a roasted corncob and a piece of sugarcane, and now they are going to look for the sheep.

It's a beautiful morning. From the first light of dawn to the rising of the sun, they watch everything in the woods come to life. The impala that live by the hundreds, on the savannah and in these woods, dart and frolic through the brush. Their finely marked, brown hides with their black and white-streaked flanks catch the gleaming sunlight; and reflect the light around them, as they leap about.

Tukula takes the path that goes down to the river, and Bonisa follows him. In a clearing in the valley, a herd of zebra has gathered. They raise their heads, to greet the sunshine of the new day. Their white and blackstriped coats glow like silk in the pure morning light.

Beautifully coloured tropical birds whistle their morning song out of joy for the breaking of a new day. Some small paradise-widow birds, with their long black tails, flutter among the branches of the trees. A crested-crane flaps its wings over the valley. The orange-yellow weaver birds spread their little wings in the sunlight, full of zest for their work as they skillfully weave their nests at the end of thin branches which hang over the river.

Bonisa's little heart is becoming somewhat happier now that everything around her is whistling and singing, and the sun plays magically with the beautiful colours of the woods. Soon they will find the sheep, and Blacky will put her woolly head in her hands and sniff her arms. She will take Blacky in her arms and talk to her. The animals will be so happy to hear her voice again. She is so eager to find the sheep. Maybe the sheep had found shelter during the night among the thorn bushes, or in a vacant kraal.

Tukula has followed the path down to the Lupandariver, where he looks around, searching. Of course, the animals must have headed North, out of the valley because the river bed, through which they would be able to go South, isn't dry.

To the Northwest lies Limpo-Lupanda, the kraal of Tukula's family, and the sheep hadn't been there. They must go up the hills in the Northeast and search there.

Tukula himself thinks it strange that he, a son of the chief, is helping a little girl from one of the many kraals in the district, to look for her lost sheep.

Would a chief's son from this country ever have given this much help and friendship to one of his inferiors? Now that Sitemba has been sick for some time, he has put a great deal of the responsibility of being chief, on his eldest son, Tukula. This is a difficult task for Tukula because his ideas differ from his inflexible father.

It was not so long ago since Tukula had paid a visit to Gambo, a wise, old chief of a small, but energetic tribe, living far South of the Lupandariver. Throughout the country chief Gambo is known as a man of "wise words." In the hut of the old chief, Tukula was taught how to rule a poor, quarreling, drunken tribe, and how to turn them into a successful and prosperous people.

Some of the wise proverbs spoken by the old Gambo are still alive and clear in Tukula's mind. Gambo had said: "Peace is the greatest blessing for a nation, for families, for men, women and children." The old Gambo told him about the foolishness of asking counsel from the witchdoctor in case of accidents and misfortune, or in asking him to point out which people in the tribe are guilty of bewitching someone.

The assistance of the medicine men often makes the sickness greater than it already is. Calling up the 'spirits of the ancestors' cannot bring peace and happiness, because only Nkulu-Nkulu (the greatest of all the great ones) is the God who rules over sickness, adversity and prosperity.

But Nkulu-Nkulu is far away and unknown. Long ago a white man, by the name of Robert Moffat, came into the land of Gambo's ancestors. He had the book of Nkulu-Nkulu, out of which he could teach the people, but that was long, long ago.

Yet, some of the wise proverbs of the white Missionary were preserved. The old Gambo ruled his people according to these proverbs and it had become a peaceful and prosperous tribe.

Tukula has learned many wise words in the hut of the old chief, and these words he repeats often to himself: "It is better for a tribe to reap the harvest, than to sharpen the spear."

Gambo told him of an entirely different way to treat his people: "Be kind to the elderly and to the children; help everyone who is in need. Then your people will respect you and you will all flourish."

Before his departure, chief Gambo had taken a costly earring out of his own ear and put it in Tukula's ear, as a sign of friendship.

"What power is there in this ring?" - he had asked Gambo.

The old man shook his head and said: "The foolish seek power and protection in amulets and charms; the wise know that wisdom, courage and power come from the Book of Nkulu-Nkulu."

Tukula had been deeply impressed by everything that he heard from Gambo. And now he needed courage to go against the old laws and customs of his own tribe, to become their leader in this new way.

Along the path, Tukula comes to a sudden stop. His eyes catch white strands of sheep wool hanging from several branches of the shrubs. The sheep had fled into the woods here, cutting right through the thick brush, leaving a trail of turnedup soil and freshly broken branches. Behind him walks Bonisa, now happily humming, for they will soon find the sheep.

Tukula follows the trail. The earth now clearly shows the tracks of hyenas and wild dogs, then... he steps aside so that Bonisa can see for herself.

Sombrely and silently, he stares at the ground under a thorn bush. There lies something white and woolly, stained red with blood. There are pieces of wool on the thorn bushes, and underneath... he looks silently at the blood-stained earth.

Bonisa looks down too. She screams, a wild cry of anguish: "No... no!." She does not see the sunlight anymore, she doesn't hear the birds anymore. She feels faint and she stumbles.

Tukula's strong hands grip her tightly. For a moment it is dark, but then light shimmers before her eyes again. She moans: "No... no!."

She sinks to the ground, screams, and cries out in horror at the terrible scene that lies before them under the thorn bush. With his knobkerrie, Tukula moves the red, blooddrenched wool slightly aside, revealing the sheep, torn apart by wild animals. The remains of the sheep reveal the black spots on its scalp. The hyenas killed Bonisa's sheep, her Blacky.

The child sits huddled on the ground and cries, exclaiming again and again: "No! No! Oh, my Blacky... my sheep." She covers her eyes with her hands so she can no longer see what is under the thorn bush.

Tukula stands by silently and waits, like men do when the women wail for children or cattle that have died. For him this discovery is no surprise; he had already expected something like this. Sheep that roam around in the woods during the night without protection, will very easily fall prey to predators.

Being a son of his nation, Tukula fears that evil powers led the sheep away from Bonisa's flock to be killed. This is the fault of Nkube, the neighbour of Vundla, because he had thrown a piece of wood into her flock.

Tukula feels responsible for the injustice that has come upon this child of his people. He contemplates the event, while the hopeless, crying child sits next to him on the ground, and the remains of the slaughtered sheep lie before them.

After a time of being in deep thought, Tukula has decided what he will do. He himself will return the girl to her family's kraal. If the child goes back alone, without the sheep, the angry Vundla will strike her fiercely with his whip. Vundla is known as a merciless man, who drinks too much and mistreats his wives and children in his drunkenness.

"Bonisa, say farewell to your sheep; we are going back," Tukula commands.

She stands up, looks one more time at the bloodstained sheep-skin of her Blacky, then follows Tukula as they return to the valley. For Bonisa, this beautiful morning has turned into a comfortless time of fear, loneliness and grief. With solemn steps, she follows him up to the derelict hut, where she had slept during the past night.

"Go into the hut and wait there until I return. Then I will take you to Vundla's kraal."

Bonisa sits down on the ground before the still smoldering fire, and waits, sad and afraid.

The penetrating rays of sunlight in the early morning of this new day, also awakens Vundla's kraal from the sombre darkness of the night. In the cattle pen the animals push their heavy bodies against the strong fence of the enclosure. They are lowing and stomping on the earth with impatience, eager to go off into the forest. There they will drink water in the valley and graze along the banks of the Bembasi river.

Nkwee and Sikla are now awake. They shove the loose door away from the entrance of their hut, and look out curiously. They hear the morning call of the animals and long to go into the woods with the herd. A couple of younger brothers who sleep in the same hut, wake up. They yawn and crawl slowly out from under the blankets made of cowhides.

Little, yellow fluffy chicks scamper across the ground of the kraal. The imprints of their tiny feet are the first tracks on the red sand after it had been swept the night before. The hens cluck to keep their babies close together. Sethu, the dog, stands with raised ears in front of Vundla's hut, waiting for his master.

A flock of birds has just come from their night perch and flies over the kraal. Their noise wakes Vundla from his restless sleep. With one powerful haul of his muscular arms he drags away the heavy door of his hut and looks with a curious, but fearful glance, over the ground of the kraal. There are no children's footprints leading from the kraal entrance to MaWanda's hut; there is nothing but the yellow chicks that scurry across the ground following their clucking mother hen.

The bright sunbeams of the new day, which penetrate through even the smallest openings of the dark huts, can't bring any happiness into Vundla's heart today. He grabs his whip and inspects the entire kraal with an angry look and threatening gestures.

The women and children peer cautiously from their huts at the ill tempered, grumbling man, who is getting more and more angry after noticing that the sheep haven't been brought home yet.

He sits at the kraal entrance, looks across the forest path from left to right, but does not see any sheep approaching. In his anger, he viciously strikes the whip on the ground.

MaWanda also looks out carefully from her hut, the baby in her arms, but withdraws fearfully when she hears the sound of the whip. Bonisa has not returned to the kraal yet. Where is she..., and where are the sheep...?

Vundla goes into the woods. Sethu, the dog, jumps and barks happily alongside his master, but with a kick and a snarl from Vundla, the animal cringes and slinks back to the huts.

The kraalhead is always the first one to leave his hut. Only after he has inspected the kraal ground for strange footprints, are the women and children allowed to leave their huts.

The three wives of Vundla begin to prepare the morning corn porridge. Still shivering from the morning chill, the children come to sit by the fire with animal hides held around their naked little bodies. However, this morning there are no happy smiles on the black children's faces. No one dares to speak out aloud. The women whisper softly to each other, while MaWanda stirs the corn mixture, her head bowed, not speaking a word.

Oh... the sheep did not come back. Did evil spirits kill them during the night in the woods? Three beautiful sheep lost! Ah... this place seems to have been bewitched and whose fault is it?

If the ancestral spirits would be pleased with them, the animals would surely have come back. Maybe the good spirits have left the kraal and the entire family has been left to the power of enemy spirits!

When Vundla returns to the kraal, angrier than when he had left, a dark shadow of fear falls over the family. The corn porridge is eaten in silence.

Nkwee and Sikla soon sneak off to the cattle pen. Just for a moment they look back with a fearful glance, then try as quickly as possible to disappear into the woods with the herd of cattle, before their angry father calls them back.

The women look at each other in fear, as the bleating from the sheep pen sounds like an urgent call to be let out. The animals see the herd of cattle leaving and they also crave for the grass and water in the valley. But who will herd the sheep now that Bonisa isn't here?

Mambi, the oldest daughter of MaWanda, is 11 years old, but is with relatives in a faraway kraal to help with the peanutharvest. The other girls in the kraal are too young. They must do other little jobs inside the kraal and gather wild vegetables in the forest.

After the meal, MaMoyo, Vundla's oldest wife, goes with her two daughters into the woods in the valley. On their heads, they carry empty calabash shells, which they are going to fill at the narrow river. MaWanda ties the carrier cloth onto her back, lets the baby slide in and goes into the woods to find wild vegetables for her evening meal.

MaThinda, Vundla's third wife, stays in the kraal. She has to make sure that the fires keep burning, and that the hens and pigs are fed. She is also teaching her 4-year-old daughter how to keep a fire going, and how to take care of the hens.

The sheep in the night pen continue to bleat as Vundla paces restlessly through his kraal, back and forth, all the time waving his whip. There is a look of fear in Vundla's eyes because he feels that the spirits are angry. Who is guilty?

4. TUKULA, SON OF THE CHIEF

In the kraal of the chief of Limpo-Lupanda, Tukula orders a young cow herder to go with the herd. Another boy is sent to Vundla's kraal with the message that the chief's son is coming to speak with him.

Tukula has a short talk with his father Sitemba, and then dresses himself in the manner of an African chief and warrior. Instead of his simple herding clothes, he now dons a shoulder drape and a skirt of leopard skin. A chain with crocodile teeth and an ivory arm ring decorate his black body. On his forehead, he wears a red leather band, in which long, colourful, rare bird feathers are displayed. A big shield, an assegai and a knobkerrie give him the look of a skillful warrior.

Sitemba commands his own headman to go along with his son as counselor. And so Tukula leaves the Limpokraal to get the little girl from the hut and take her back to her family's kraal.

The message that the young boy brings from Limpo into Vundla's kraal causes quite a stir within the family. Tukula is coming with the headman of his father to speak with Vundla. What does that mean?

MaWanda, who has just returned with the wild vegetables, and MaThinda, are busy, at Vundla's command, making the kraal as clean as possible. The children are taken to their huts with strict orders not to leave the hut for as long as their father has visitors.

Vundla paces with excitement, shouting out orders and cracking his whip. He calls for beer. He wants to drink beer, lots of beer; and he has already drunk so much this morning. The strong beer clouds his thoughts and awakes in him a desire to fight.

Finally, MaThinda manages to get the restless man into his hut. He must wait there until the announced visitors arrive at the kraal.

Fortunately, MaMoyo and the two girls return in time with their gourds full of water. They lift the full gourds from their heads in front of MaMoyo's hut and carry them to the cooking hut. They wipe the beads of sweat from their faces and look with satisfaction at the many liters of fresh water they now have.

The women disappear into their own huts. There is a strange silence in the usually busy and lively kraal. Then the sound of footsteps is heard on the forest path. All eyes peer sharply out of the dark huts. A shock goes through the women as they see the athletic figure of a warrior equipped with his weapons, come out of the forest.

The young warrior stands at the kraal entrance while his headman walks in. He pauses for a moment. MaMoyo, as eldest of the women, comes out of her hut. She walks over to the headman and greets him. He tells her that the son of the chief has come to speak with Vundla.

MaMoyo makes a slight bow. She goes to her husband's hut and asks him to receive the visitors.

Trembling, Vundla goes outside. He heads toward the kraal fence to greet the guests in African fashion. It turns into a long conversation about the health of the cattle, the harvest and many other things.

After this greeting, Tukula gives his assegai and knobkerrie to his headman, who puts the weapons in the forest outside the kraal fence. This is the sign that the visitor has come with a peaceable purpose in mind.

The children hardly dare to move but their eyes follow everything that goes on outside. They know Tukula very well. He is the shepherd of the big herd of cattle and a friend to all animals and children in the area. But how they see him now... no, they have never known him in this way.

Tukula stands there, superior and solemn, with the appearance of a king and commander. He carries the big Zulu shield in his left hand.

42

For a moment, Vundla looks with respect at the fiery young warrior. But suddenly Vundla sees someone standing behind the warrior. His temper flares up again. "Ah...!" he screams, "It's you...? Where are the sheep?" He becomes quiet, but then, his voice booms even more loudly through the silence: "Speak! Where are the sheep?"

There is movement inside the huts. Women and children stretch themselves in order to see why Vundla has become so angry. Oh...! Whispered calls of surprise break the silence. Oh... they see Bonisa! She stands there, small and huddled, hiding behind the warrior and the big shield.

"Speak!" bellows Vundla's voice. "Where are my sheep and where is my whip?" In his rage, he takes a step sideways to strike the girl to the ground with one mighty blow, but the shield is instantly there to protect her.

With calm but powerful voice the son of the chief speaks: "Do not harm her. She is under my protection. I will tell you about the sheep."

Vundla trembles with rage and hollers furiously: "I have the right to punish my children and I will deal with them accordingly." He goes to his hut and returns with his whip.

Tukula, the young warrior, stands inside Vundla's kraal, unwavering, like a statue, as black as midnight. "My spear," - he commands his headman.

As swift as lightning, the headman disappears into the woods and returns immediately with the spear, which he puts in Tukula's right hand.

With eyes flashing, Vundla lifts his arm. The whip cracks through the air and is meant to come down upon Bonisa.

With one swift movement, Tukula stops the striking lash with his shield. The young warrior then holds his spear in a forward thrust position and with a strong voice commands the drunk brute in front of him: "Bow down... or die!"

Frightened screams sound from the huts. The women tremble and the children begin to cry. Bonisa's teeth chatter with fear.

Vundla lowers his whip in bewilderment and sees that the raised arm of the warrior holds the spear point towards him.

Again, Tukula orders: "Bow down... or die!"

Vundla bows and lays his whip at the feet of the chief. The women and children leave their huts to bow down beside the kraalhead, before the young chief who rests the tip of the spear on Vundla's back, as a sign of victory.

Bonisa, who is still standing behind the shield, now walks to her family and kneels down beside MaWanda. So, they all acknowledge, according to their centurysold unwritten laws, the dominion of the conqueror over the entire family. After some time, with the signal of Tukula, they stand up.

There is only one handmade chair in the kraal. MaMoyo offers it to the young warrior at Vundla's command. Tukula takes the seat. His headman and witness stand beside him. It gets very lively inside the kraal. The women bring a big calabash with home-brewed beer and every member of the family gives a small gift to Tukula. A nice, full corncob, a few stems of sugarcane, a watermelon and several lovely wicker baskets, woven by the women. Vundla gives the whip, with which he intended to beat his daughter, to Tukula as a sign of his submission.

Then Tukula, after drinking the beer, goes with his headman into Vundla's hut for a meeting, and Bonisa follows her mother into their own hut. Never before was this hut a safer shelter than on this day. The glowing fire is more welcoming than on other days. The red flames are like the friendly, gleaming lights of the good spirits. Together they sit on the straw mat by the fire.

Bonisa nestles closely against her mother. Her small, black curly head rests against MaWanda's arm. Oh... how happy they are to be together again! All the little brothers and sisters from the other huts come to sit with MaWanda around the fire. They look with wonder at Bonisa, who is safely home again.

Ah... there must have been a protective spirit that went along with Bonisa, and that good spirit allowed Tukula, the son of the head chief, to go along with Bonisa, to protect her. Ah... that Tukula, he will become a great warrior. Yes, they had seen how with one quick movement of his shield he had stopped the terrible lash of Vundla's whip. If that whip had come down on Bonisa's head and shoulders, oh... then she would have screamed in pain and might have become ill. But now... ah, now Bonisa is a sister to be proud of.

After several hours, the meeting in Vundla's hut ends. The young warrior and his headman leave the kraal. Out of respect for the visitor, the women and children walk outside and make a deep bow for Tukula, staring after him in awe. The stately appearance of the young chief, his stern, powerful gaze and the strong muscular hands that clutch his spear and shield, demand respect.

He wishes the family the protection of Nkulu-Nkulu and commands them to come with all their worries and hardships to his kraal at Limpo-Lupanda. There he will give them advice and tell them how to deal with their difficulties.

The sheep in the night pen are bleating constantly; today they will have to be fed inside their enclosure. However, help will soon be needed to herd the sheep in the forest, and Bonisa is still too small to do it by herself, Tukula had said. Vundla must find other help to herd his sheep.

Therefore, Vundla decides, that same afternoon, to make a trip to the family with whom Mambi is staying. She has to come home. Vundla has another plan in mind about which he has told no one.

Out of fear of the young warrior, who came to his kraal with the authority of the chief, he had bowed to Tukula's authority. During the conversation in the hut he had to promise that he would not punish Bonisa. He had to promise that he would drink less and work harder along with the whole family, because Tukula wants better harvests, cattle, and hutbuilding in all of the Lupanda valley.

Although he has bowed before Tukula, in his heart remains bitterness, because three of his beautiful sheep have been lost. Three sheep are worth a lot, and not only that, he is afraid that at the end of the corn harvest MaWanda's father will come to collect the rest of the dowry. That will cost him three cows, or... his oldest daughter.

Ah... he has a good plan. He will go to the witchdoctor who lives far from here. He will ask him who is responsible for all the misfortune they have had. Of course, he will have to pay the witchdoctor one or two goats, but if the medicine man can drive the evil spirits out of the kraal, then the whole family will become happier and will have better fortune. He will order MaMoyo, his eldest wife, to take care of everything during the days he will be away on the long trip to the family from where he will bring back Mambi.

As twilight falls over the woods and the villages, the families gather around the woodfires for their evening meal. Bonisa sits beside her mother by their own fire. Oh, how happy she is that the terrible, fearful night in the dark forest is past. Bonisa has lost three sheep and her beautiful Blacky is dead, but she has found a new friend. Tukula, the son of the chief, is now her friend and protector.

Late in the evening in the huts of the Lupanda-valley all the people have long gone to sleep and everything is quiet. MaWanda and her child sit for many hours by the wood fire inside their hut. Bonisa sits very close to her mother and tells her everything that happened during the evening and the night before.

46

5. THE WITCHDOCTOR AND THE 'WHITE MAN'

With a heart full of fear, Vundla makes the trip to his relatives. He is afraid that his ancestor spirits will no longer protect him. He is sure evil spirits have killed his sheep, along with the help of the hyenas. Something has to be done to please the amadhlozi so that the evil spirits will leave his kraal. That is why he wants to go far away to the powerful medicine man to ask for advice.

For many centuries heathen Africans, without the liberating love of the Gospel, have lived in fear of offending the spirits. Vundla and his family also live in this bondage, constantly threatened by dark powers, which have to be placated. There is an endless struggle to obtain the protection of good spirits and the fear of being harmed by enemy spirits.

After several days, Vundla returns to the kraal with his eleven-year-old daughter. Two days later, the medicine man arrives to find out who is guilty, who is responsible for the many misfortunes in the kraal.

MaWanda, who is in the woods this afternoon, picking wild vegetables, is suddenly gripped by inner restlessness and feels drawn back to the kraal. "Come," she tells Bonisa, who is helping her, "I have to go to back to the kraal. I feel that someone is waiting there for me."

Upon arrival in the kraal, she stands frozen for a moment. She groans pitifully when she sees the witchdoctor sitting outside Vundla's hut. A sense of coming disaster takes hold of her.

The eyes of the medicine man flash wildly when he sees MaWanda standing there. Immediately he stretches out his arm to her and speaks with a voice that seems to come out of the ground: "There...! She is the guilty one!"

A dreadfully heavy silence falls upon everyone inside the kraal.

With her head bowed MaWanda stumbles into her hut.

"We will ask the amadhlozi why she is guilty," the witchdoctor continues in the same low voice. (Most witchdoctors are ventriloquists.) He stands up and Vundla follows him to MaWanda's hut. The medicine man squats down at the entrance of the hut. He takes a dirty, little bag out of the pouch that hangs from his loincloth belt, and empties it in front of MaWanda. Little bones of monkeys and snakes scatter across the red sand.

Inside the hut, Bonisa huddles closely against her mother and intently watches what the witchdoctor is doing.

He gathers the small bones together and shakes them in the hollow of his hands. Then with a dull muttering, he throws them into the hut in front of MaWanda.

The poor woman moans and groans in fear. Bonisa clings more closely to her mother.

The medicine man now enters the hut and studies the way the bones are spread out on the ground. From this he must decide the wish of the spirits. This takes long very long. Deep wrinkles spread across the face of the man, as he mumbles some hard to grasp words. MaWanda trembles. What will happen?

Finally the witchdoctor lifts his head, looks sternly at MaWanda and speaks: "The spirits of your ancestors wish to have the spirit of your son in their spirit world."

A cry of deep misery escapes from MaWanda's lips.

Again the medicine man throws the bones on the ground in front of MaWanda; this time to read how the child has to die. "Ah... it is clear! The child may no longer have any food or drink. After several days the spirit of the child's body will be released into the spirit world. Then the amadhlozi will be pleased and Vundla will have good fortune."

As payment for his advice the medicine man demands one healthy cow, which he will choose himself from the herd when Nkwee and Sikla return home with the animals.

That evening, the hard-hearted medicine man leaves Vundla's kraal with the cow, to return to his own village, leaving behind a wearied and stunned family.

The days that follow are full of deep misery for MaWanda. She can no longer bear to hear the lamentable cry of the hungry child, but she has no choice. Her husband Vundla despises her. He says that she has never brought any fortune to his family and that he still has to pay the price of several cows for her dowry. She definitely isn't worth that much.

She can't work as fast as the other women; her child Bonisa has let the sheep wander off; and now the spirits have demanded the life of their little boy. No, Vundla doesn't have one more friendly word to say to her; he resents her.

Mambi does not want to live in MaWanda's hut. She would rather be with MaMoyo because she is afraid that the spirits of MaWanda will harm her. Only Bonisa stays close to her mother and tries to help her as much as possible.

One morning, after Vundla has gone into the woods to hunt, MaWanda tells her daughter that she must go to Tukula's kraal to ask for advice on whether the little brother might be allowed to live or should really die. Bonisa must stay in the hut to watch that the fire doesn't die and to make sure that her little brother doesn't cry too much. Ah, it's so difficult!

After MaWanda has left, Bonisa kneels down beside the little boy. Oh, he is crying so much! His little voice is hoarse from wailing; his tiny fists lay clutched against his narrow, little shoulders. She tries to put the old antelope-skin blanket over him, so that the flies and insects will not bother him so, but he wildly kicks it away.

His crying turns into dreadful screaming, just like the sound of the hyenas at night. Little brother will probably die soon; that is the demand of the medicine man. The spirits of the ancestors want

49

the spirit of her little brother with them in their spirit world.

Bonisa still remembers how horrified her mother was when the medicine man said that her little brother was not allowed to have food and drink any more. Father Vundla had spoken harsh and angry words, because MaWanda did not want her son to die. Then her father had become angry, he had taken a stick and wanted to beat MaWanda... Yes, and then Mother had said that it was all right. She was afraid of the stick, of course, and of the medicine man, and of the spirits. Since then, her little brother has not been fed.

But occasionally, when no one is watching, MaWanda pours a small handful of water into his mouth. Sometimes mother takes him in her arms and walks to the opening of the hut. She looks at her son for a long time, and then she cries, but no one is allowed to notice...

"Bonisa..., you have to go with me," a voice says suddenly from the opening of the hut.

It scared her, because she was thinking of the medicine man and her little brother, and so she didn't notice that MaWanda had come back. She gets up quickly, stays a small distance away from her mother and asks: "What should I do for you?"

Mother's orders are short and Bonisa obeys them immediately. "You have to pile the wood on the fire so that it will glow for a long time, and carry along the basket with corn dough, the sleeping mat, and the antelope blanket."

As Bonisa rolls everything neatly together, MaWanda takes her son in her hands and lets him slide into the carrier cloth that she has tied onto her back. She puts the basket of corn on her head and lays the rolledup mat and blanket on top. She then commands Bonisa to leave the hut.

The other wives of Vundla stand Sombrely and silently in front of their own huts and watch them go. They know where MaWanda is going and that makes them afraid. Oh, as soon as Vundla finds

50

out, he will be very angry!

With long strides, MaWanda follows the trail past the kraal of Nkube; Bonisa follows her. Neither of them says a word. Bonisa had sometimes gone far into the woods with her father and his flock of sheep, with Nkwee and the cattle, but not as far as her mother is going now. No... she has never been this far.

Mother walks on and on... and the woods become darker. The trees are so tall and the leaves on the plants are so big that she begins to feel small and scared.

The trail is very steep and leads down to a small river. There, MaWanda sits down to rest. She takes the little boy out of the carrier cloth and tries to get him to drink some water that she scoops with her hand from the river. But he doesn't want to drink. With his little fists, he pushes her hand away. He kicks and screams. Tears squeeze from his dark eyes and roll down his skinny, wrinkled body.

MaWanda's head leans over the little boy as she sobs quietly. Bonisa is also very sad. Everything is so different this morning and little brother's crying carries so far through the jungle.

Mother lifts little brother into the carrier cloth again and wades through the river. The water is not high. They can easily walk over the stones in the riverbed.

The trail on the other side of the river is very narrow and soon there is no path at all. Sometimes MaWanda stops to look at the sun and the trees. She searches in every direction.

The underbrush is so dense here that it scrapes along their legs and arms. Bonisa grabs her mother's skirt very tightly. She is afraid in this strange, distant jungle, and mother just keeps walking..., on and on through the dark forest.

The trip takes very long. They go through another river, but this one is wider and the current is stronger. MaWanda feels Bonisa holding her tightly as they go through the water churning around them. Fortunately, there are no crocodiles to be seen and they make it through unharmed. They must go on..., even further South. Bonisa is getting tired; she can barely go on.

Suddenly, MaWanda stops... She stares ahead... Bonisa sees something too... It is big and white... It glistens in the sunlight.

"Here is the house of the 'white man'," MaWanda says faintly.

Oh, Bonisa's eyes become wide with awe. She has never seen anything like it. She is only used to the round huts in her own kraal and those of the neighbouring kraals, but this house is so big... and white... And there are many children and women sitting on the ground at the front of the house. She becomes timid and apprehensive. She puts her hands over her eyes and doesn't dare to look.

MaWanda seems to be wary as well. She sits down on the ground among the bushes and stares intensely at the white building. "Here lives the white man who has strong medicines to drive the evil spirits out of people," she tells Bonisa.

For a while they sit quietly together among the bushes, until little brother begins to cry loudly. MaWanda now has no choice but to get up and walk on.

Oh..., the white man himself is walking toward them! His face is fair, his hair is white, and his clothes are white, too. Bonisa keeps her eyes covered and peers cautiously through the cracks between her fingers.

The white man talks kindly to her mother. He looks at her little brother, lays his hand on little brother's head and says: "Oh..., Oh..." What would that mean? Maybe a magic word?

Ah..., fortunately a black nurse comes out of the white house and joins them. She immediately speaks to MaWanda in her own language. Then they enter into the white house. Bonisa hides her head in her mother's skirt.

Jhula, the black nurse, takes little brother in her arms and into a room of the hospital where there are so many strange, but beautiful looking things. Bonisa doesn't know where to look. The safest thing for her is to keep her hands over her eyes. Only when the white man is not looking at her, does she dare to move her hands slightly.

"Come and watch while I am washing little brother," says Jhula while she walks over to a sink.

Bonisa clings to her mother's skirt, but the white man tells her that she should go over to see her little brother. She takes a deep breath and shyly walks over to nurse Jhula.

Jhula turns something shiny and then... clear, splashing water pours into the sink. Bonisa can't hold back a gasp of surprise, but Jhula laughs and says: "Ah... you have never seen water that flows from a tap. You should stay with us, and then I will show you many nice things!"

When little brother is cleaned and washed, the white man examines the little boy while he asks MaWanda many questions. "What is the name of the little boy?"

"He can't walk yet," answers MaWanda.

"Will he get a name once he is able to walk?" asks the Missionary.

"Yes."

"Why doesn't he get a name now?"

"Maybe he will die."

"If you give him no food, he will surely die. Why don't you give the child enough to eat?" The voice of the white man sounds stern.

MaWanda whispers softly: "The corn is all gone."

"Do you eat very little yourself?"

MaWanda nods and sighs deeply.

"If there was plenty of corn in your kraal, would you then give the little boy enough to eat?" asks the Missionary.

"Yes, then I would give him plenty," the woman says in a monotonous voice.

The white man does not trust the answers MaWanda has given him. He turns to Jhula and tells her in a language that Bonisa cannot understand: "Take the girl outside and ask her why her little brother isn't getting any food."

"Come, we will go outside to the other children," says Jhula to Bonisa who is afraid to go.

With a little kindness and a few jokes in their own language, the nurse helps Bonisa overcome her shyness. Bonisa sees how the other native children at the hospital are walking around happily, singing and playing games.

It doesn't take long before Bonisa tells Jhula that the medicine man was in their kraal and now little brother can no longer have any food because he has to go to the spirit world.

"Ah... Ah...! And your mother is afraid of the medicine man. Ah... our white doctor at the hospital is a wise man. He says that medicine men are liars. And I believe that is true," Jhula says with a determined voice.

"Our white doctor has a beautiful book, full of words of great wisdom. In that book is written about the great King, Who makes sick people healthy again. The medicine men in our own country are liars!"

Bonisa watches and listens attentively to Jhula and asks: "Is the white man a white witchdoctor?"

"Ah..., no, he is an Umfundisi, a servant of Nkulu-Nkulu God. Stay with us in the hospital, then you can also listen when Umfundisi reads out of the Book."

For a long time, the Missionary continues to talk with MaWanda inside the hospital. She is tired and slouches in the chair, her head sadly leaning forward. Her hands move nervously over her skirt.

"No..., oh no..., I can't stay here. I have to go back to our kraal. Before the night falls I must be home."

"The trip is too far for a woman as tired as you," he says kindly. "Stay here just one night, and tomorrow, on the new day, you can go back."

But there is a frightened look in MaWanda's eyes as she says: "No... oh no, my husband doesn't know I'm here and he will punish me if I'm not home to sweep the ground of the kraal before night fall."

"Then I will take you back to the kraal in the hospital Jeep and tell your husband that Bonisa and the little boy will stay at the Mission post until he is strong again."

An intense fear is etched on the face of the poor woman. She puts her hands over her face and groans, then she gets up and walks on to the veranda. Just then, Jhula walks over with Bonisa who is laughing happily and admiring everything around her.

Jhula, who has been working at the Mission hospital for several years, is a wise girl and almost immediately understands what is the matter.

While Jhula tries to calm the crying woman, the Missionary joins them on the veranda. "Listen to Umfundisi," Jhula says comfortingly. "He is a man of wise words. He will speak wisely to your husband, Vundla. Umfundisi will take medicine along for all the sick people in your kraal."

The despairing look in MaWanda's eyes fills Jhula with compassion so that she turns and asks: "Umfundisi, could I come along to take this woman back to her kraal?"

"Ah..., that's fine, Jhula! Then we will at the same time take two other patients along who are ready to go home today."

MaWanda waits at the Mission post for a few hours with Bonisa and the little boy. They are shown the big hut where Bonisa will sleep tonight.

An old African woman comes towards them, takes MaWanda's arm and says: "Ah, you are from that country where the light is not yet shining. But do not fear. The nation that lives in darkness will see a great light! He, the Light of the world, has come into our land of darkness."

The old woman wipes her eyes with the corner of her skirt. Tears fill her eyes as she speaks: "Have you ever heard of the 'black dancer' of Kimba? That was me. I used to do nothing but dance, feast, and drink beer. At all the chiefs' feasts, the 'black dancer' was invited to sing for the spirits. Yes, I was black..., black with sin. I lived in the land of darkness, but now the light has come. My black heart is now full of light... Inkosi Jesu (King Jesus) brought light into my soul and He seeks more black sinners to bring them into the light."

The old, wrinkled hand is still holding MaWanda's arm as the shaky voice pleads urgently: "Oh, do stay with us here at the Mission post. I will tell you about the great Light and Umfundisi will read out of the Book of Nkulu-Nkulu."

All these words sound strange to MaWanda. She doesn't know what they mean, but says: "My children are going to stay here," she points to Bonisa, "Tell her about that light. Help her to find that light."

Then she stumbles out of the door. She looks for the shade of a Tshabela tree under which she can sit and wait until the Missionary and Jhula ask her to get into the hospital Jeep. Oh, this is strange! She trembles.

One of the other women, who is coming along with them, has been in a car before and is used to it; she assures MaWanda that it is not dangerous. However, she does hold a cloth in front of her nose and mouth because she believes that the evil spirits have put poisonous gas in the motor of the car. This gas is dangerous to inhale, say the women. It makes you weak and unable to work hard!

This creates a new fear for MaWanda. She presses the corner of her skirt so tightly against her nose that she is barely able to breathe. She feels the threat of the evil spirits around her wherever she goes.

As the motor of the car begins to rumble, MaWanda's eyes widen with fear. She is scared and wants to jump out of the moving vehicle. Jhula holds her back and tries to calm her down.

The other women are laughing. They often ride in the car of the Mission post and are used to the sound of the motor.

Close to the Lupanda river the Missionary stops the car in front of a kraal. Here lives one of the women who is now healthy and very thankful to be home again.

While the Missionary goes along with her to greet the family, MaWanda whispers to Jhula: "Take good care of my children... Do not let the white man come to our kraal... When the moon has been dead and comes alive again, I will come for the children... I am going home alone now..."

She quickly lets herself slip out of the Jeep and disappears immediately into the dense jungle.

Jhula watches her go. She understands the woman's fear of the witchdoctor and her husband, because she has taken her child, who was ordered to die, to the Mission Post without his permission.

Poor woman; thinks Jhula. Tonight during the evening service at the hospital, we shall pray for her to be saved from fear and darkness.

And so MaWanda returns to the kraal, alone.

6. AT THE MISSION POST

A new life has begun for Bonisa at the Mission Post. The first days are somewhat strange, but the old African woman, MaRunda, is very friendly to her. The Missionary often talks with her about her little brother and her mother so that her fear of all the new things at the hospital quickly disappears.

There is so much to see and hear every day that she hopes her little brother will have to stay in the hospital for a long time. Each day, new patients come to the Mission Hospital, and the sleeping hut where Bonisa sleeps, is now completely full. Umfundisi has said that no more patients can be admitted.

Yet when more sick people come, the Missionary's wife says, "Ah, let them stay too. These people are so sick and they have been fooled so many times by the medicine men of their own tribe. Let us help them!"

There is a girl of twelve. Her arm is so big and swollen that when Umfundisi and the nurse look at it, they are appalled. The girl is terrified because she fled from her village and has come alone to the Mission Hospital.

The medicine man was to come back to their village to treat her sick arm again, but she was so worried... The medicine man had already cut several times into the swollen arm and rubbed in powder and herbs to get rid of the evil spirit. A throbbing pain began in her arm and became worse and worse. In fear of the witchdoctor, she came to the Mission Hospital.

Umfundisi drains an abscess on her arm and after several days the swelling goes down and she feels much better. A thankful and happy smile spreads across her face as she is allowed to return home again in good health.

One afternoon, as Bonisa is walking around the hospital grounds, she hears a dreadful cry coming from the bushes. She walks towards the sound, pushes the branches aside and sees a boy lying on the ground. He groans and calls out: "My eyes..., oh, my eyes... oh, help me!"

"Ah..., " says Bonisa, "Who are you?"

"Oh, my eyes..., my eyes...! Where am I?"

Jhula, who usually sees and hears everything that happens around the Mission Post, appears and squats beside the young boy.

"Who are you? How did you get here?" she asks.

"Oh, please help me...! Oh, my eyes!"

Jhula runs to the hospital to tell Amos, the African nurse, that he must bring the stretcher, and then she goes into the laboratory to find the Missionary. "Oh, Umfundisi..., oh, his eyes are so sick," she says out of breath.

"Who's eyes?" he asks.

"Ah..., the eyes of the boy who is lying outside. He has so much pain."

"Tell me where he is, Jhula."

A while later the Missionary kneels down beside the boy who is lying partially hidden under the bush. Carefully they lift the boy onto the stretcher that Amos has brought.

The boy looks terrible. His skinny arms lie lifeless alongside his body. His ribs stand out sharply beneath his black skin. His belly, swollen from a hunger edema, is covered with old rags.

But his eyes are worst of all. The skin around his eyes is red and badly swollen. The dirt from the infection has crusted around the eyelids. A number of tormenting flies crawl freely over his eyes. The boy has no energy left to use his hands to swat the flies away.

"What is your name, little friend?" Umfundisi asks him.

"Oh..., my eyes! My eyes! There is fire in my eyes!" is all the boy can answer.

"Take him to the treatment room, Amos. First we will do something to stop the pain in his eyes. The poor boy is suffering a lot of pain. But tell me, Amos, how come his eyes are so sick?"

"Ah..., why do you ask, Umfundisi? I will give you the answer that is already in your heart. Are the medicine men in our country not liars and deceivers? Their poisonous medicines have damaged this boy's eyes. But you are a doctor of wise words and good medicine. Maybe you can still heal his eyes," Amos answers hopefully.

"You know that I can't heal eyes," says Umfundisi. Only the Lord, the great Physician, can do that. But we will use the best medicine and pray to the Lord that He, by His power, will heal the eyes."

In the small treatment room of the hospital, the Missionary puts some eye drops in the boy's eyes to stop the pain. He cries with fear: "Oh no, my eyes...! There is fire in my eyes!"

"Ah..." says Amos, the African nurse, "Do not be afraid of the doctor. He will take the fire out of your eyes. You know, when there is a fire, you throw water on it and the fire goes out. Now..., that is what Umfundisi is doing to you. He is putting drops of

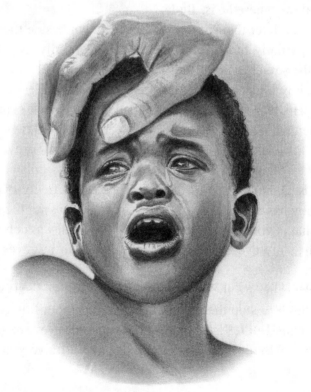

special water into your eyes to stop the burning. Be brave! Soon you will feel that the fire in your eyes is gone." The boy is calmed by Amos' words and tries to be quiet.

"Umfundisi," Jhula asks somewhat shyly, "yesterday you read in the Holy Book that the Lord says: 'Without Me you can do nothing.' Why not first ask the Lord if He will help us to make these eyes better?"

The Missionary looks at her thankfully for a moment and answers: "You have listened well, Jhula, when I read out of the Bible. Yes, we shall pray for the boy; maybe we can still spare his eyes, with the Lord's help."

The boy is lying on the simple, wooden table. The burning pain in his eyes has eased somewhat. He sighs and speaks slowly: "The fire is dying... but I don't see any light... I'm in the land of darkness."

"Yes, my little friend," says the Missionary, while his hand takes that of the boy, "You are right. You are in the land of darkness. Do you long to see the light again?"

"Who wouldn't?" sighs the boy.

"Ah..." Amos answers quickly, "if you don't know you are in the dark, you won't long for the light."

"We shall pray that you might see the light again," the Missionary says.

The three of them stand around the treatment table: the Missionary, his trusted helper Amos and Jhula, the African nurse. Their heads are bent in reverence while the Missionary makes known the need of the child to the great Physician with plain words in the language of the sick boy. With deep reverence and dependence on the blessing of the almighty God, the white man prays that the light may be brought back to the nearly blind eyes. Very earnest and sincere are Umfundisi's words as he prays for the Light of the Sun of Righteousness to come into the dark heathen heart of this sick boy.

"Where is the 'Great Physician'? Who can bring new light to my eyes?" asks the boy. Then a sudden panic shakes his body, as he cries: "No... it's not possible...! No, there are no cattle left!"

Questioningly, the Missionary looks to Amos who has a broad smile on his black face and almost immediately answers: "Ah... Umfundisi, he thinks that cattle have to be paid for the treatment. Ah... there was never an African medicine man who helped sick people without the payment of cattle or corn."

"Tell him, Amos," says the Missionary, "that I am a servant of the 'greatest Medicine man' in all of Africa, but that this Physician does not ask for the payment of cattle or money. He helps sinners who are in need. He Himself has paid for everything that is necessary to heal the sick and to bring Light to dark hearts."

Amos, who himself was once a spirit-worshipper and had become a Christian, tells the boy in simple terms about the sacrifice that the Son of God made, by which He paid the full price to heal and deliver sinners. "But..." Amos says with much emphasis, "As long as you don't know that your soul lives in darkness, you will never long for the Light that only the Lord Jesus Christ, God's son, can give you."

Later that afternoon, Zenja goes to a small intensive care room because he needs special care for several days.

Some time later, as Amos is walking near the small hospital and passes by the bushes where they found Zenja, he sees a black face with sharp, piercing eyes looking at him from among the branches. He moves the branches aside and looks into a nervous, startled boy's face.

"Ah...! Are you sick?" asks Amos. "Don't stay there under this bush. Umfundisi can't help the sick from here."

"No, I'm not sick. I brought my brother here. What is happening to him?" the boy asks shyly.

"Is Zenja your brother? Which medicine man ruined his eyes?"

The voice of Amos sounds threatening.

"He was an expensive medicine man," says the boy.

"Tell me, how many cows did you pay to let your brother's eyes be ruined?"

"We paid a beautiful cow, but his eyes became worse each time. I slept with him in the hut and last night he complained and cried all night that there was fire in his eyes. I couldn't sleep for even a moment. He was to go to the same witchdoctor again today, but he didn't want to. That's why I brought him here."

"Why didn't you bring him when his eyes were only a little bit sick? Didn't you know that our Umfundisi has the best medicine?" Amos questions him further.

"The medicine man will put a curse on any family that brings one of their sick to the Mission Hospital," he answers.

"Why do you bring him now? Aren't you afraid that a curse will come over you?"

"No... nobody will know that I brought Zenja here."

"What will you say when you get home?"

"Ah..., when I take my sick brother through the lonely woods to the medicine man and a lion tries to attack me, don't I have to flee? And when I return later on to look for my brother and I don't find him, ah... maybe the lion killed him."

"Ah... ah..." answers Amos. "You are planning to tell lies when you go home. Lies are sins against the law of God. You have to tell your family that your brother is here and that Umfundisi has good medicine for ailing eyes. When Zenja is better, he will go back home. Where is your kraal?"

The eyes of the boy widen with fright: "No..." he says, shocked, "We live to the South... far to the South, but Zenja must never come home again."

With a sudden leap he dashes out of the bushes and runs into the forest, as fast as he can. But... he goes North!

Amos continues with his work. He understands that the boy

doesn't want to tell where he lives, out of fear of the medicine man. No one will know where Zenja lives, will Zenja himself ever want to tell?

Every evening at six o'clock, in the veranda of the Mission Hospital, the Missionary holds a short service for all the patients. The wards open out on to the veranda and the patients who are able to walk on their own gather there. Family members, who are staying in the huts at the Mission Station, also come at the sound of Amos' call. They too come to listen to the reading from the Holy Book of God. There are open windows in the sick rooms along the side of the veranda and the doors of the rooms are opened so that patients who must stay in bed can hear the service.

Jhula has moved Zenja's bed right in front of an open window and whispers to him: "Listen carefully, Zenja. Umfundisi is going to read from the Bible. He will pray for you too."

Zenja cannot see because of the bandages on his eyes, but his ears are alert; he does not want to miss a word of what the Missionary is about to say.

More than a hundred dark women and children and several men are crowded together on the red, polished floor of the small hospital. The Missionary, his wife, Sister Mary and Sister Rhoda, are seated in the middle of the veranda. Amos, is beside the Missionary. The old Christian, MaRunda, sits on her mat, near Sister Mary. And there, in that big group of people, closely crammed together, Bonisa is sitting opposite the Missionary, the Missionary's wife.

Oh, this is always the most beautiful moment of the entire day, because now Umfundisi is going to say something and she wants to listen. She wants to hear more and more about the stories from the Holy Book!

The old MaRunda has told Bonisa that Umfundisi is not a white witchdoctor, as she thought at first, but a servant of the almighty

God, Who lives in heaven. And the great King, Jesus Christ, is the mighty Physician who heals sickness and pain, and is able to take away their fear of the spirits.

The Missionary stands up. He has the book of God open in his hands and for a moment he looks around to see if everyone is quiet and ready to listen.

With great attention, many black eyes are focused on the white man as he reads from God's Word, about the great King, who has spoken: "Come unto me, all ye that labour and are heavy laden, and I will give you rest. Take my yoke upon you, and learn of me; for I am meek and lowly in heart: and ye shall find rest unto your souls, for my yoke is easy, and my burden is light." (Matt. 11:28 30.)

Then the Missionary says: "We shall ask the Lord for a blessing on His Word that we have just read."

Everyone, including the children, stands up, while Umfundisi prays. It is a prayer pleading for mercy; a prayer for the mighty working of God, the Holy Spirit, in the hearts of the people. Only the Holy Spirit can give new life to the hearts of sinners, and kindle a new light in their deep, spiritual darkness; a light, which will enable them to believe everything that is written in God's Word, as truth.

Umfundisi's prayer is a plea at the Throne of Grace, to God who has said: "Ask of me, and I shall give thee the heathen for thine inheritance, and the uttermost parts of the earth for thy possession." (Ps. 2:8) Here is a prayer, in the name of the Lord Jesus, to make these ignorant heathen an inheritance and possession of Christ, so they will learn to bow to Him as Savior and King, so that His praise and glory will be sung by many nations.

After prayer, everyone sits down again, and the Missionary begins to discuss the texts that were read. For a while Umfundisi looks calmly over the people until it becomes very quiet. Everyone is now looking at the Missionary, who is about to speak.

"Have you ever been tired?" He asks. "So very tired that you longed for rest...?"

The people's attention is now noticeable. Their gaze is focused on the Missionary, who speaks with calm, clear words in the language of the people.

"When you have filled a large vessel with water in the river or at the well, and have carried it on your head, a long, long way to the kraal, you become tired, and want to be rid of that burden of the water vessel you long for... rest..."

Umfundisi looks at the people who are sitting on the floor to the right and to the left. He pauses briefly before he continues to speak. The women nod in agreement and Bonisa thinks of her mother. Ah... MaWanda is always so tired when carrying water from the river.

The Missionary goes on: "When you have to carry heavy baskets of corn, and take large bundles of firewood from the forest to the kraal, on your head, then you long for rest. Your head and your back ache under the heavy load, so much that you can barely carry it any longer. Oh, how you long to put off the burden. If someone would say to you then, when you are tired and nearly exhausted: 'Give me the burden that you carry on your heads, and I will carry it for you so that you can rest', Oh... would you not be glad and grateful?"

The women and the girls look at Umfundisi and nod their heads. Yes, they are often very tired from the heavy loads that they must carry.

"But," continues the Missionary, with a voice so urgent that they are all compelled to listen, "there is a burden that is much, much heavier than the heaviest load of wood, water or corn that you have ever carried. That is the burden of sin that you all carry along in your life. And what is sin...? Do you know what sin is?"

He pauses again for a moment. His eyes search the dark, earnest faces. "Who can tell us what sin and the burden of sin is?" He repeats his question.

The people on the ground become restless. They know what

Umfundisi means.

Then the old MaRunda stands up. Somewhat shakily she leans against Sister Mary's chair, and whispers something into her ear.

Sister Mary asks her to speak more clearly so that everyone can understand her.

MaRunda's voice is still soft as she answers: "Everything that is against the will and the holy law of God, that is sin."

"Amos, repeats her words so that all can hear it."

Amos' voice sounds clearly through the hallway and through the open windows of the sick rooms.

"And what is the burden of sin that presses one down so heavily?" Umfundisi asks further.

MaRunda's answer is soft again, but Amos repeats it with a clear voice.

Now, the Missionary turns to MaRunda and asks her if she herself has felt that burden of sin.

Oh yes, she had carried a heavy load that had pressed down her soul. She had danced for the chiefs at the heathen feasts of spirit worship. Her whole life had been sin against God's holy law. Because of this, the condemnation of the law had come upon her life. That was like an unbearably heavy burden upon her soul. She had felt it when a Missionary had come into their area and preached about the holy law of God, the Ten Commandments. Afterwards she couldn't dance, drink beer and feast anymore because her heart had been touched by the Spirit of God.

The Missionary had gone back to her village a few more times and told them about the great King, about 'Inkosi Jesu'. Fear of - but also love for the Almighty God, of whom they had never heard before, had come into her soul; also a sadness such as she had never felt before. A sadness for her sins the many..., innumerable sins against the law of the great Creator.

Then Umfundisi had read aloud from the Holy Book, of the blood of God's Son that cleanses from all sin. She believed that only through that blood could she be saved from the heavy burden of guilt and fear that pressed upon her soul. By faith, the power of that blood had come into her dark heart. The burden of sin had been taken away from her, and peace had come into her soul. Guilt and fear had been removed. Light had come into her soul. - The Light of Jesus Christ, the Sun of righteousness. - Oh, how different her life had become then. There came peace, happiness, a love for the Lord and for her neighbours and a longing for the Word of God.

Amos repeats with a clear voice the testimony of the old, converted dancer, MaRunda. Long ago, she was known all over the land as the 'black dancer' from Kimba, and now, through the work of the Holy Spirit in her soul, she has become a Christian!

The two white nursing Sisters are deeply moved by MaRunda's words and silence falls over all who are sitting on the ground. Bonisa moves slightly forward to get a better view of MaRunda. She can't take her eyes off the old woman. Oh, MaRunda is now looking back at her and Sister Mary looks at her as well. Would they notice that she is listening so attentively? Bonisa does not want to forget anything she has heard! As soon as she returns to her own kraal, she will tell everything to her mother.

The Missionary starts to speak again, but first he looks over all the people to see whether they are listening. "Have you felt sin in your soul as a heavy burden from which you would like to be delivered? Then it says in God's Word: 'Come to me, all ye that labour and are heavy laden, and I will give you rest."

Bonisa wonders: "Is Umfundisi looking at me while he is asking this?"

A few verses of a Psalm are sung. The harmonized sound of the male and female voices blends into a beautiful choir. It fills the hallway, passes through the windows of the hospital, and can be heard al over the Mission Station as a song of praise and honour to God.

7. BONISA, A LOST SHEEP

At the end of the evening worship, as dusk settles over the Mission Post, the kerosene lamps on the veranda and in the wards are lit. The nurses attend to the sick who are lying in the hospital rooms while their family members go to the guest huts to sit by the woodfire for a little while yet.

Bonisa sits on the ledge of the veranda and takes in all the activity around her. Her little brother is lying in one of the hospital rooms in his crib, and she is allowed to wander around for another while until Sister Rhoda and Jhula shut the hospital doors.

She has so much to think about! She sees and hears so many new things about which she has never been told in her own kraal; specially what the Missionary had said a few days ago, after he had read from the Holy Book. She is still thinking about it. About the Great Shepherd who never leaves His sheep, and always brings them safely home.

Umfundisi had spoken about the sheep of the Good Shepherd. The people who believe in Him and follow Him will never be lost. But those people, who are not of the flock of King Jesus, will perish into eternal darkness.

Bonisa cannot forget those words... After all, she is not a sheep of that Great Shepherd...; she is a child who worships the spirits. She wears an amulet around her neck; it protects her because it contains the power of her ancestors' spirits, but then you are not a sheep of the flock of Inkosi Jesu.

A hand rests on Bonisa's shoulder. She looks up and sees Umfundisi standing beside her. His friendly face looks down at her. Feeling shy all of a sudden, she stands up and bows to him. A smile spreads across his face. He sits on the wall and lets the girl sit down beside him.

"Bonisa, do you like staying with us at the Mission Post?" he asks.

It takes her a while to answer. Her hands shuffle along the wall, and while she stares at the ground, she says softly: "I'm not a sheep of Inkosi Jesu and sometimes I'm afraid to be in the dark."

The answer of the small, dark girl moves the heart of the Missionary. He quietly prays for wisdom to speak with this heathen child.

"Why are you scared of the dark, Bonisa?" he asks her. "Aren't you allowed to sleep in your hut at night by the fire? There is no danger, is there?"

Bonisa can't give an answer right away. Oh, how she wants to tell everything to this kind Missionary... about her sheep that wandered off and about that terrible, fearful night in the dark woods. But maybe Umfundisi will be angry with her too when he hears that. She sighs deeply a few times, lets her legs dangle restlessly back and forth, and continues to look at the ground.

The Missionary waits calmly beside her as he realizes that there is something inside the child that she cannot talk about very easily.

Jhula has finished her rounds with the patients. She shuts the doors of the hospital and walks out across the veranda with Sister Mary. They stand still at the ledge.

Sister Mary sees her husband sitting beside Bonisa on the ledge and looks at him questioningly. The Missionary gives her a sign to tell her that she shouldn't wait for him. She understands that her husband wants to talk with Bonisa. Sister Mary knows that personal talks with the Africans are very important for their Mission work. There is usually too little time to talk with the patients and family members. However, when it is possible from time to time, such moments must be taken advantage of with a prayerful heart.

The kerosene lamps on the veranda cast a soft glow in the fast approaching darkness. The buzzing of insects in the lamplight and the chirping of crickets in the grass announce the arrival of the African night. Behind the hospital, the sheep are bleating; they

70

have just been driven into their pen for the night.

Bonisa lifts her head and listens. She hears the sheep. Oh... now it seems as if she is home again in Vundla's kraal, on that terrible night... Now she wants to tell Umfundisi everything.

Sister Mary has prepared the evening meal in the small Mission home and looks out through the window. It's taking a long time for her husband to come home. Is he still sitting with Bonisa on the ledge, or has another patient been brought in?

Outside is the dark silence of the night that has just begun. A donkey brays, the sheep bleat in the night kraal, a nightjar flies with fluttering wings past the window.

Out of the darkness, a faint light is slowly approaching along the forest path that connects their dwelling to the hospital. That must be her husband.

Sister Mary walks outside toward the light. She carries a lantern too, because there may be snakes on the path. In the dry, narrow riverbed, halfway along the path, they meet each other.

"You waited a long time for me, Mary."

"Yes, but I knew you were doing important work," she answers understandingly.

"You mean listening to Bonisa?"

"I thought you were talking to her."

"Oh... I listened more than I spoke." Then, with a voice full of emotion he continues, "O Mary, I can't say what I felt when that child told me about her fears and the hard life she has had at home in her kraal. Poor, poor child...! A lost sheep without a shepherd... wandering in dark Africa."

They walk together along the forest path that leads to their house. There they stand for a long time. The sky is cloudy and dark. Rising and falling drumbeats echo through the night. There is so little time to talk together about their great task of Mission work to make known the Gospel message to these needy people.

Now, standing on the top of the Lupanda hills, in the dim lamplight, the Missionary tells his wife the story of Bonisa that he has just heard.

A mild breeze drives away the dark clouds and reveals a deepblue night sky. The shadows of the forest and hills are silhouetted against the night sky.

"Mary..., how many thousands of people live in all those huts, as far as we can see, to the North, the South, the East, and West...? Moreover, all of them have a never-dying soul. Oh, how little we can do for such a great number of heathen. We must pray that the Lord will send out more labourers. The harvest is so great... so very great... and the labourers are few."

"Yes, and the help that we can give at our Mission Post is no more than a few drops of water in the ocean of misery and death in this part of Africa," she responds.

"It's so hard to send the sick, who have come during the last few weeks, back to their far away villages," she continues, "especially the women with little children. I can't keep taking them in. The rooms are overcrowded; the people are lying tightly pressed together between and under the beds. We must try and build an addition to our small hospital..."

"We have no money left, Mary."

"The Lord has heard our prayers before and helped us so often. Let us trust in Him. If we can take more people into the Mission Hospital, then we can teach them from God's Word too. Oh, how much I would like to help thousands of people in our hospital and tell them about the power of the love of Christ, who came into this world to seek and to save those who are lost. Ah, how many people in these forests die uncomforted because they are not saved? In those thousands of huts are sick women and children in great fear, misery and loneliness because they do not know the prayer:

I'm poor and needy, yet the Lord
of me a care doth take:
Thou art my help and Saviour,
my God, no tarrying make."

The two Missionaries stand on the hilltop, staring across the dark woods to where lie the huts of the people who suffer such needless agony.

They stand there for a long time. They speak about their great task; - to tell the heathen, who are still in spiritual darkness, about the holy law of God and about the Lord Jesus, the Great Shepherd who has fully kept this law - . They feel the weight of each human soul. There is an intense and holy longing in their hearts to bring even the most ignorant heathen to the knowledge of the Gospel. They know that in their labour, they are dependent on God's blessing and that only God, the Holy Spirit can open the hearts of the people and make them new creatures in Christ Jesus. They have received instruction from their King: "Go ye therefore, and teach all nations, baptizing them in the name of the Father, and of the Son, and of the Holy Ghost: teaching them to observe all things, whatsoever I have commanded you."

In the Missionary's home that evening, the two kneel in prayer to tell the Almighty God about the worries of their labour and about the needs and miseries of the many sick people in the hospital. With intense desire they pray for the fulfillment of the promise that the Lord Jesus Himself once gave to His disciples: "And other sheep I have, which are not of this fold: them also must I bring, and they shall hear my voice; and there shall be one flock, and one shepherd."

It is a prayer of faith, asking if the Great Shepherd will still add sheep to His great flock, of which He has said: "My sheep hear my voice, and I know them, and they follow me, and I give unto them eternal life; and they shall never perish, neither shall any man pluck them out of my hand."

The following days at the hospital are so busy that the Missionary cannot find time to talk with Bonisa again. A boy, who was attacked in the river by a crocodile, was brought to the Mission Hospital. His thigh was bitten and torn, but fortunately, with treatment his leg was saved. Another boy had cut into his foot with an axe while chopping wood; two of his toes were cut off. And a young man, who often had nosebleeds, was brought in. Oh... everyone shivers at this. There must be very evil spirits living inside his body that push the blood out through his nose.

Even Sister Mary and Sister Rhoda are so busy all day long that they can't find time to talk with Bonisa.

However, at the evening service in the hallway of the hospital, the Missionary explains the Bible in plain and simple words, so that even the children can understand. He sees the attention on Bonisa's face. He always talks about the Great Shepherd who looks for lost sheep, also in Southern Africa, to add to His great flock. Those sheep will never get lost again! Inkosi Jesu, the Great Shepherd is speaking to the children of this nation: "Suffer little children, and forbid them not to come unto me: for of such is the kingdom of heaven." (Matt. 19:14)

During the day, when the sun is shining and the birds are singing in the woods, old MaRunda often goes for long walks through the woods, over the hills that lie South of the Lupanda-river. MaRunda knows exactly where to find the places in the woods where the best reedgrasss grows for weaving beautiful baskets and sleeping mats.

Bonisa is often allowed to go along with MaRunda who shows her where to find the reedgrasss. She teaches her which tree roots have the sap she needs to make dye. A small portion of the gathered reedgrass must be dyed red or blue to weave patterns into the baskets. MaRunda teaches Bonisa creative skills; how to twist bark fiber into string; how to make wrapping cloth and skirts from the bark fiber of Baobab trees.

74

The days pass quickly, and during all this work and their treks through the woods, old MaRunda often tells Bonisa about the great Light of the Gospel that has come into her soul and her life, through faith in Christ.

Whenever MaRunda and Umfundisi talk about Inkosi Jesu, the whole world appears beautiful to Bonisa. But in her heart the fear of the dark night lives on, the night that will come and never turn into a joyful morning if she does not become a sheep in the flock of the Great Shepherd. Umfundisi has talked so often of the mighty King who has said: 'Let the children come unto me.' Umfundisi has asked her if she longs to go to this King.

Oh, then she listens carefully, but how can she long for a king whom she can't see, a king out of the book of the Missionary? And if you are a sheep in the flock of that Great Shepherd, you are no longer allowed to wear an amulet and that frightens Bonisa. Oh no, she would never dare to take the amulet from her neck because without the protection of her ancestors, the enemy spirits will attack her. No... she doesn't dare.

But, if you do not become a sheep of the Good Shepherd, you will perish in the dark night that never ends. A dark night that will be much worse than that night when she had to look for her sheep in the woods. So a struggle goes on in the child's heart; - a struggle between light and dark.

Then something wonderful happens deep inside Bonisa. Something breaks open in her dark, fearful heart. A small flame of new life begins to glow in her young soul. A new life awakens her spirit with love and longing toward Him who has said: 'Suffer the children to come unto me...'

A strange feeling of longing and love for Inkosi Jesu overwhelms her. Oh, how she would like to be close to Him now and to be one of His sheep, never to wander away from Him again...

Bonisa is in the woods. MaRunda has sent her to pick reedgrasss because the old woman has a sore foot and cannot walk very far.

At the foot of the hill, East of the Mission Post, the dark girl kneels. This is how Umfundisi and MaRunda have taught her. God is holy and when people pray to Him, they bow before the Almighty God to ask the greatest of all kings for help and protection.

The child's prayer is short and simple. She only asks: "Inkosi Jesu, may I come close to You? I want so much to be a sheep of Your flock and to always stay with You."

After Bonisa has returned to the Mission Post and has taken the reedgrasss to old MaRunda, she looks for Umfundisi to tell him about her prayer in the woods. But a sick boy has just been carried in and is being treated by the Missionary; so, Bonisa sits on the veranda and waits.

The grandmother of the boy has come along and is also sitting on the veranda. The screaming of the frightened boy can be heard from the treatment room. He is in a lot of pain. Oh... he cries so much!

"Ah..." whispers the grandmother to several women who are waiting their turn to be helped by the Missionary. "There is a snake in his stomach. He is possessed. Our medicine man in the valley couldn't chase away the snake, so we brought him here. Ah... the white man will need strong medicine to drive this evil snake from his body."

Bonisa looks at the grandmother and says: "Umfundisi is much stronger than the medicine man, because Inkosi Jesu helps him."

"Eeeh..." says the old woman. Scornfully, she spits on the ground. "You are small. What do you know about the power of our medicine man?"

"Inkosi Jesu is the greatest Medicine Man. He can do anything. He has healed Zenja's eyes which were ruined by the witch-doctor."

The old woman moves a little closer toward the girl. She hisses like an angry cat and sneers: "Eeeh... don't speak to me like that, or I will put a curse on you."

"If you are a sheep of Inkosi Jesu, you cannot be cursed and you can never be lost," responds Bonisa with her first childlike faith.

The grandmother turns her back to Bonisa, disgusted with the young girl. The grandmother looks toward the woods where, far away, beats the steady rhythm of the drum. Somewhere the tamtam is being played to keep evil spirits out of a kraal.

Bonisa continues to wait, but Umfundisi does not come out; he is with the sick boy who believes that there is a snake in his stomach. He groans and cries out again: "He's biting...! Oh, he's biting me!"

It is evening and in the hallway, the evening worship for the patients has ended. All the women and children go to the huts for their night's rest. The patients who are able to walk on their own go to the big sleeping hut.

Bonisa stands by the wall of the veranda where Umfundisi has spoken with her several times. She wants so much to tell him about the light that has come into her heart her love for Inkosi Jesu. However, she finds it hard because she cannot yet clearly understand how she can come to the Lord Jesus and always be with Him.

The Missionary, who has put in a busy day at the hospital, is tired and longs for the tranquility of his home. He hastens outside across the veranda. In his haste, he pays little attention to the girl who is staring intently at him as she stands by the wall. He walks past her, but realizes a short time later that he has left a few important notes in the laboratory, which he needs to make up a report. With the same haste he turns around and heads back toward the hospital. Then he sees that Bonisa is still standing in the veranda. Ah, he will tell her to go to MaRunda in the sleeping hut.

But suddenly he sees the pleading expression in the child's dark eyes and the tense lines in her face. He now notices from the way she is standing that she is waiting for him. He hesitates. He needs to go home to do some writing. He has to write a detailed report that will demand his full attention for several hours.

Should he again use up his precious time off to talk with this child? Ah, he has done it so often. Each time he hopes to notice some changes with the Africans from preaching the Gospel to them. The people appear happy and grateful for the good treatment they receive when they are sick. They listen out of politeness when he reads from God's Word. But a true change in their souls, a new spiritual understanding of the message of the Gospel, is very rare. This makes him feel dejected at times. Especially when he notices strong opposition from all the witchdoctors in the region. They turn the people against the Mission and spread mistrust toward God's Word.

In the last glow of the setting sun, he sees Bonisa standing in front of him. Unavoidably the thought comes to him again: "Poor child, a lost sheep without a Shepherd... wandering through 'dark Africa'..." During Bonisa's several-weeks-stay at the hospital, the light of the Gospel surrounds her, but will it continue in the life of this child when she, with her ignorant heart, returns to the darkness of her old family life? Will she perish, without a Shepherd, into eternal darkness?

These thoughts stir his soul and give him the need to speak with her once again. "Do you long for your mother and family again, Bonisa? Or do you want to stay with us at the Mission?" he asks her.

There is a wonderful sparkle in the child's eyes, as she says: "I long for Inkosi Jesu. Will you tell me how I can come to Him?" In her voice, he hears a touch of the longing in her heart.

The white man is moved by her unexpected answer. He is filled with joy! Could the heart of this heathen child be opened to find the Lord Jesus as her King and Redeemer?

Bonisa sits on the wall of the veranda to show that she wishes to continue talking there.

The Missionary takes a seat beside Bonisa and silently prays to receive wisdom from God, the One who sent him, to speak with this child. "Bonisa, the Lord Jesus is a holy and a mighty King. He has said: 'Suffer the little children to come unto me...' If you long to go to Him, then the great King will ask you to give Him something. Do you want to do that?"

She is shocked when Umfundisi tells her this. For a moment she stares away in deep thought, away into the distance, where behind the forest and streams lies her family's kraal.

The Missionary looks at Bonisa's small, dark face. It is filled with tension and lined with thought as she stares away into the woods. The sad, dark eyes of the child look up at him, and she answers: "Ah... I can't give Him anything. My mother doesn't have anything, and my sheep... my Blacky is dead... I myself have nothing either."

"Bonisa, the Lord Jesus doesn't ask for cattle or any other possessions. Only medicine men do that. The Lord asks you for something you do have. He asks for your heart. Will you give Him your heart?"

"Yes."

In that single answer lies a tone of the deep surrender of her entire soul to the great King.

The evening hour slips fast away into the darkness of the African night a night in which the moon is 'dead'. The silhouettes of trees and shrubs are still faintly visible, but soon they have vanished into complete darkness. This scene gives the Missionary an opportunity to talk about the Light.

"Bonisa, when it is dark in your mother's hut, without a single ray of light or glow of the fire, can you see if the ground of the hut is dirty?"

The child smiles somewhat surprised: "Ah... no."

"When a chief wants to come and visit you, does your mother first clean the hut so that all the dirt is gone? Yes, of course, for a chief everything has to be clean and tidy. Your mother can't see the dirt when it is dark at night. But during the day, when the light shines into the hut, she sees the dirt and she can remove it before the chief comes.

So it is in your heart, Bonisa, just like your hut in the kraal. You long for Inkosi Jesu to come into your heart, but should your heart not be clean to receive the Spirit of that holy and mighty King, Jesus Christ? Is there also a lot of dirt and evil to be cleaned out of your heart?"

Earnestly thinking, the girl looks up at Umfundisi, and a lovable smile of innocence spreads across her young childish face. Her dark eyes light up with glee as she says: "No, my heart is now clean and white, because I am kind to you."

The Missionary notices with surprise that even this child of about eight years old has already accepted the heathen idea that a Zulu king had taught his nation with his speech: 'When I am friendly and my face shines with happiness, my heart is clean and bright and innocent. But when I am angry and hostile, my heart is dirty, dark and full of guilt.'

Umfundisi has often noticed that when he speaks with heathen Africans about sin against God's law, and about their guilty and unclean souls, that a very friendly expression comes into their eyes... They think that they are clean and innocent. The evil that is committed against a holy God does not even give them a sense of guilt in their soul. Proverbs 30:12 comes to his mind: 'There is a generation that are pure in their own eyes, and yet is not washed from their filthiness.'

"Bonisa, if you think that your heart isn't dirty, then that is because it is still dark in your heart. You can't see the wrongdoing, just as in your mother's hut. She can't see the dirt on the ground in the darkness of night. But when the light shines in, she can see it and clean it. As long as it is dark in your heart, you can't see the evil of sin. But when the Lord lets His light shine in your heart, oh, then you will see all the evil inside.

It is night now, Bonisa. You must go to the sleeping hut, but first we will ask the Lord if He will shine His light into your heart so that you can see for yourself whether it needs to be made clean."

The Missionary lets Bonisa walk with him to his small office in the hospital and there they kneel down together at a plain, wooden bench. A white Missionary and a dark child bow before the Lord. The Missionary prays; the girl listens. Bonisa's ears and heart are open; each word penetrates into her young soul.

Umfundisi prays with simple words in the native tongue of the girl, asking God to let His Holy Spirit shine into her heart so that she may know her sins and find Christ as her Savior.

Then Umfundisi picks up his notes from his office and takes Bonisa to the big sleeping hut. Old MaRunda stands waiting at the door and grumbles that she is late. But Umfundisi lays his hand on her arm for a moment and says kindly: "Good night, Bonisa. Pray fervently for the Light."

"Good night, Umfundisi. I won't forget."

8. THE AMULET

An epidemic of tropical dysentery, whooping cough, and measles has swept through the Lupanda district. Hot, stormy winds drive the infectious organisms from one village to the next. Clouds of dust and dirt are driven by the wind, only to whirl down further on to the huts in the next village. The warm wind carries along swarms of mosquitoes and black flies through which infection spreads quickly.

Many Africans seek refuge at the Lupanda Mission Post. Some women and children are surrounded by a whole swarm of flies when they arrive at the Mission hospital. These flies torment the infected eyes of the children.

The forest ground in front of the Lupanda hospital looks like a refugee camp. A great number of women are sitting there with children who shiver feverishly, waiting for help. The sick rooms are filled with patients with not an inch of space to spare. The sick also lie between and under the beds.

Umfundisi, Sister Mary, Sister Rhoda, Jhula, and the other African nurses are very busy. The danger of infection is great. Therefore, sister Mary tells the people that the patients with dysentery must be taken into separate isolation huts. The people must also make certain that the black flies do not land on their food because that will also spread disease.

The patients look at each other in wonder and they begin to laugh. The women whisper among themselves: "Oh, those foolish white people; they think flies can make us ill! Ah... those white people don't understand that all diseases are brought by the spirits. The magic power of the evil spirits spreads disease! But the medicines of the white man are good, very good, much better than that of our own medicine men."

That is why they have brought their sick children to the Mission hospital. The number of patients becomes so great that there is no shelter available anymore. All the night huts are full. Many mothers have to spend the night under the Mopani trees behind the hospital.

The wood fires burn brightly in the night. The red flames reach high into the dark night. The patients lie close to the fire on their sleeping mats, some under blankets, others under antelope hides. The men and boys have made a wide circle of thorn branches for a protecting wall around the group of people who must sleep outside. Sometimes there is the crying of jackals and the eerie laughter of the hyenas near by, but several men keep watch by the fires, armed with heavy clubs. The animals keep their distance when they see the fires and do not dare to push their way through the barrier of thorn branches.

After several days the hospital runs out of medicines. That is a great ordeal. Both the Missionary and his wife feel dejected. The Missionary is worn out. "O, Mary," he says to his wife one evening, "we can no longer give injections, the medicines are nearly gone and I have no eye ointment left for the children. What will the people say now when I must let them go back to their huts, without treatment or medication, sick as they were? When I went into their kraals, I asked them to come with their sick to the Mission hospital. And now that they have come, we can't help them."

Even in difficult times of trial and tribulation there is faith in God's almighty power in Sister Mary's heart. She speaks encouraging words to her husband, telling him that God has a wise purpose for everything, even in times of trial. Maybe the Lord is now showing the people how truly great His almighty power is.

That evening, at the worship in the hospital, the Missionary makes known his concerns in prayer to the Lord. He asks for help for the many sick people who are here at the hospital. He tells Him of their needs now that the medicines have run out.

He prays to his Father in heaven to help the patients see and believe that God only is their helper in time of need.

Old MaRunda cannot sleep tonight in the big hut. She is also filled with concern for the many sick people for whom there are no more medicines. The African woman kneels on her sleeping mat and prays to God for help.

Bonisa whose sleeping mat is next to MaRunda's, listens with reverence to the words of this old, black Christian, and quietly prays along with her.

When the first morning light is barely visible, MaRunda awakes. She leaves the sleeping hut and walks over to the house of Umfundisi. The Missionary is standing in front of the window, staring at the sky as the early morning light drives away the darkness of night. He folds his hands and prays anew. Worry fills his heart. The new day is coming and there is no medication for the many, many sick.

A soft coughing noise in front of the window attracts his attention. A person is standing there; probably a patient who needs help. He walks outside and sees old MaRunda. Somewhat concerned, he asks her if she is sick.

Trembling, she raises her black, wrinkled hand, and points to the heavens. "Umfundisi," she says, "there lives Nkulu-Nkulu, the Lord Jehovah, Who sees and hears everything. He has said: 'Call upon me in the day of trouble and I will deliver thee.' Nkulu-Nkulu will help us and all the heathens will know that the hand of the Lord has done it."

She lowers her hand. Tears run down her black face as she says: "There is but one God, the Lord Jehovah. He will help us."

Without saying anything else, she hobbles back, with bowed head, exhausted. Her words bring silent joy into the heart of the Missionary. He watches her as she disappears over the path and into the forest. She does not take the path to the hospital, no... Umfundisi knows where she is going.

East of the hospital, among the Lupandahills, is a quiet place to which the old MaRunda often resorts. There is a holy piece of ground in the quietness of the woods, under the rustling tops of the Tshabela trees. A place where she, a 'King's daughter' from Africa, often gets down on her knees to worship God. The former 'black dancer' has now received the Lord Jesus as her King and Savior. Her sins are washed away by His holy blood. Her heart is filled with His love.

This quiet place in the woods, where she often prays for the conversion of her people, for whom she has so much love, is also the place where she prays for Bonisa's deliverance from spirit worship. This morning she goes there again to pray for medicines for the sick. She believes that Nkulu-Nkulu, the Lord Jehovah, will help.

An hour later the Missionary is called to come quickly to the hospital. A man has been brought to the hospital, badly burnt. During the night, when he was drunk, he had fallen into the fire in his hut. By the time the family answered his screams, parts of his back and shoulders were already severely burnt. They brought him a great distance in an ox sled to the hospital. The black skin is completely burnt away in many places. The raw flesh contrasts brightly with the black, blistered skin.

One of the man's sons says: "Umfundisi, you have preached in our kraal about your almighty God. Now we do not take our sick father to our medicine man, but to you. Will you ask your almighty God to heal our father?"

While the Missionary examines the man, Jhula whispers to him: "Oh, Umfundisi, we do not have any more ointment or bandages."

"Let Amos take the patient to the treatment room," he answers.

Meanwhile, he goes to his small office. He sits at the table with his head in his hands and prays. "Lord, You know everything... What must we do today without medical supplies...? Lord, it is for

the honour of Your holy Name. Let the heathen not be able to say that we worship a God who does not have the power to heal their sick. Lord, help us, so that the heathen will know that You alone are the true God... Lord, it is all for the honour of Your Name."

There is a commotion going on outside, in front of the hospital. A sled approaches, pulled by four oxen, and led by an African who is yelling loudly.

The Missionary stares through the window at the commotion. "Another one who is sick? And no supplies left," he groans.

A couple of Africans lift a heavy crate from the sled. With much clamour, it is placed on the veranda. A second crate follows..., another..., and another.

"Umfundisi!" Jhula exclaims. "Umfundisi..., gifts from Holland!"

He staggers outside. He is tired and barely able to walk steadily. The many tensions and short night rests of the past days have taken their toll. There are four crates, closed tightly with iron bands. Written on the crates is: A GIFT FROM HOLLAND FOR THE LUPANDA MISSION HOSPITAL.

Roger, the gardener, and Tshebo, the ox driver, are allowed to open the crates. With pliers and hammers they carefully go to work; the wood mustn't split. The crates can be used again for storage space.

Umfundisi leans against one of the pillars of the veranda. He is dizzy and has a terrible headache. His wife, Sister Mary, begins to unpack the crates.

When the contents of the crates are well visible, she looks at her husband. Tears well up in her eyes, and Jhula who is standing beside her, whispers: "The Lord Jehovah has heard our prayers."

In front of them stand four crates full of medicines, bandage materials, and boxes full of syringes and ampoules for injections that are so urgently needed.

Sister Mary opens a little white carton a few tubes of ointment for burns slide into her hand. She gives them to her husband. She cannot speak; her heart is overflowing with emotion.

The Missionary takes the tubes of salve and a few injection ampoules to the treatment room. For just a moment, he folds his hands around the medical supplies and words of gratitude come forth from his heart: "Thank You, Lord. Thank You."

Now he must immediately help the man with the burns. Jhula helps.

The patients who are able to move around on their own are very interested in the crates and their contents. They peer into them with curiosity. Ah... magic medicines from the white people. There is strong, magical power in those crates... better medication than that of their own medicine men.

The small group of curious patients becomes larger and larger, and joining them is the old MaRunda. She looks into the opened crate, but her old eyes cannot make out everything there. Sister Mary, who heard from her husband that MaRunda had already been at their house early this morning to tell him she had faith that Nkulu-Nkulu would help, now walks over to the old woman and shows her the medicines and rolls of crepe bandages.

MaRunda stands motionless for a moment. She blinks and her lips move in silent prayer. Then she looks around, tells the people on the veranda that the God of the Bible is the Almighty God, Who sent His servant Umfundisi to this country to heal the sick. He has also heard our prayers for the need of medicines and has brought us these crates filled with new medical supplies.

MaRunda says: "Have we not prayed for His help? We will now thank Him."

The wrinkled hands of the old African woman rest on the edge of the wooden crate. With a clear voice and with simple words she thanks the Lord in her native tongue. When her prayer to Nkulu-Nkulu is finished, she testifies of her faith in the Son of God and of the light and peace in her soul. She asks the people to put their

88

trust in the Word of God and no longer in the amulets with their supposed protecting powers.

MaRunda's voice sounds earnest as she speaks out a warning: "Choose whom you want to serve. If it is the Lord God, serve Him, but no longer wear a charm. You cannot love Inkosi Jesu and continue to wear charms, thinking that they can protect you."

There is a silence on the veranda. The people listened carefully to MaRunda when she spoke of the Mighty God, Who sent the crates with supplies to heal the sick.

But now she tells them that they must choose between the King from the Book of Umfundisi and their amulets... ah... now they turn their heads and walk away. No, they will never discard their amulets, no... because if they do, the spirits of their ancestors will no longer protect them.

Most of the women return to their fires to prepare the corn meal, and to take care of their children. Bonisa leans against the wall of the hospital veranda. With her hands tightly clasped together, she looks at old MaRunda. Oh, she heard very well what MaRunda said; again and again she hears those same words: "You can't love Inkosi Jesu and still wear the amulets that hold the protection of spirits. Choose now who you want to serve. If it is the Lord God, serve Him and no longer wear an amulet."

The hospital Sisters ask Roger and Tshebo to take the crates to the medical supply room so that they can further empty the crates there. MaRunda leaves to find a spot by herself in the shade of a Mopani tree where she can weave her baskets.

Bonisa goes alone into the forest. There is a great struggle in her young heart. She does not want to be with others now. She also does not want to wander with Zenja through the woods now as they have often done before. Bonisa wants to be alone. She walks far in the direction of the Lupanda valley where the reedgrass grass grows very high. Among the hills, hidden in the tall, yellow grass, she begins to pray to Inkosi Jesu.

She has done this often. She has prayed for the light, as Umfundisi told her. The light has come into her heart and that has made her afraid. She has seen her own heart and it is not so clean. In her heart are so many sins against the holy law of the Lord Jehovah. She has tried to make her heart clean by obeying the commandments of the law that MaRunda has taught her. But it's not possible. She cannot be obedient.

Umfundisi has read from the Holy Word of God: "Love your enemies." Oh... she can't do that. Nkube, their neighbour, is her enemy. He made her sheep scatter away from the flock. She hates him; she cannot possibly love him.

Since her heart is so full of sin and so full of terrible thoughts, Inkosi Jesu would probably never want to come into her heart. Her heart is too dirty for Him, and still... still there is such a love for Him in her heart. With a childlike desire, she longs to come closer to Him.

But, if Inkosi Jesu does not want her as one of His sheep because her heart is so full of sin, and she decides not to wear an amulet any longer, then there is no one to protect her. That is why she does not dare to take off her amulet.

In the young soul of this little girl, who lives in the midst of 'dark Africa', there is a struggle between light and darkness. The Great Shepherd gathers His sheep from amongst all nations and kindreds and peoples and tongues. He will, by the power of His Word and Holy Spirit, drive away all the darkness of their sin and unbelief, including that which is in her heart.

The Sun, before whose rays
the deepest darkness yields
That One Who will have vict'ry,
is Christ, th' eternal Light

It is evening. After a grueling and busy day, the Missionary stands under the trees behind the hospital to lead the evening service with the patients. He is exhausted, but there is reason for heartfelt gratitude towards the Lord. Great relief has come today with the arrival of the crates of medicines and supplies.

All the people at the Mission hospital come to listen. There is not enough room in the veranda of the hospital at this time, so they must go outside and sit under the trees. The windows of the big ward are wide open. In this way the patients who must stay in bed can listen too.

Zenja sits outside. His eyes are completely healed. Beside him sits Bonisa and beside Bonisa, old MaRunda. Umfundisi is going to speak about Jesus Christ, the Son of God, Who was crucified on the cross of Calvary. He was brought as a sheep to the slaughter.

By this message, Umfundisi teaches that a sinner, who wanders in deep darkness, can yet become one of His sheep. He was laid in the grave but is risen again. He lives forever. He is the Great Shepherd, Who says: "My sheep hear my voice, and they know me, and they follow me."

With great earnestness, the Missionary asks the people who are sitting before him: "Are you a sheep of the Great Shepherd, Inkosi Jesu? Oh, if you are not a sheep of His flock, you are lost and will perish in the night of eternal darkness. The Great Shepherd calls you to come to Him. Does your heart long for Christ, but are you afraid that He does not want to receive you as one of His sheep, because your heart is so dirty and full of sin?"

As the darkness falls, the people continue to listen, sitting quietly around the open woodfires. The Missionary sees two dark figures sitting in front of him. He cannot make out who they are. But he doesn't have to know. He must preach the Gospel to everyone. The Lord himself will open hearts, and with the power of the Holy Spirit the Gospel message will penetrate their souls. He repeats his question: "Are you afraid that Christ does not want to receive you as His sheep, because your heart is so dirty and full of sin?"

Bonisa's ears and heart are wide open. Umfundisi's words touch her young soul.

"Oh... but that's why Christ died on the cross. His blood flowed on the hill of Calvary so that poor, wandering sheep with hearts full of sin would come to Him in faith. His blood can cleanse your heart. His blood can give you new life to serve Him. Jesus' blood means His life, which He laid down at Calvary's Cross. He suffered and died the death, which his guilty sheep deserve to die so that they will live forever in His flock. He rose from the dead and is now alive for evermore. Is your heart joined by faith to Jesus Christ, like a sheep that follows its shepherd? Then let go of everything that binds you to the service of the amadhlozi, of sin and satan."

Now the people are becoming restless. Ah... Umfundisi may talk about Inkosi Jesu, the Good Shepherd. That sounds nice. They will listen to that. But he must not tell that they cannot honour the spirits of their ancestors, no, they will not listen to that.

The Missionary then reads a Psalm in their native tongue; it is a song of praise for the blessing they have received today, the crates filled with medical supplies.

The strong, harmonized singing of the Africans echoes through the woods. The soft evening breeze carries the sound until it floats away into the silence of the night.

Umfundisi watches the dark figures, sitting in front of him on the ground. He hears their beautiful singing; he sees their dark faces glow in the red flames of the fire. Have these Africans only opened their mouths in singing God's praise? Are their hearts still closed to Christ? He does not know. There is sadness in his soul for the many, many people, who wander as lost sheep without a shepherd in this 'dark Africa'.

The Missionary does not realize that among the many people sitting there, is a little girl who weeps with joy for the words that he has spoken.

92

Bonisa's head is bowed, her hands folded, and she hears deep in her heart again and again those words that Umfundisi has spoken: "His blood can cleanse your whole heart. His blood can give new life, to serve Him. Is your heart joined by faith to Jesus Christ, just as a sheep follows his shepherd? Then let go of everything that binds you to the service of the amadhlozi."

Bonisa now feels in her young heart the wonderful power of the blood of God's Son that once flowed on Calvary. It fills her heart with true love for Inkosi Jesu. The power of His blood gives her new life. The love of the great Shepherd for her, binds her soul to Him, to love Him and to follow Him for always, as a sheep follows its shepherd.

The choice of her heart has been made. The Lord Himself lets her feel His love and now she will not wear an amulet anymore. The amulet that holds the power of the spirits that were to protect her, is now a dead weight around her neck. She does not want to wear it any longer. Through faith, her soul is joined in love to Inkosi Jesu. She trusts only in Him and His protection.

The women rise and go with their children to the sleeping huts. Bonisa remains seated beside old MaRunda. It is quiet under the trees behind the hospital; only the soft crackling of the fire can be heard. The dying embers cast a soft glow over the old woman and the young girl.

Now Bonisa wants to tell MaRunda about everything that has come into her heart this evening. Her words are so childish and plain. The love for her amulet has died. A new life, the love of Inkosi Jesu, the Great Shepherd, now completely fills her soul. She loves Him, because He first loved her.

MaRunda's trembling hands undo the amulet necklace around Bonisa's neck. As the necklace slides off into MaRunda's wrinkled hand, the beads knock against each other with a dull clunk. The old woman stands up and Bonisa follows her without saying a word. For a moment, the amulet of white and red beads lies in MaRunda's opened hand, then the old Christian leans forward and lets the necklace fall into the fire.

Bonisa stares after it. She sees how the smoldering fire forms new, little flames. The red tongues of fire lick along the wooden beads and engulf the amulet in their devouring blaze.

In a matter of seconds, the amulet is charred to shapeless black ashes.

9. HOME AGAIN IN THE KRAAL

The full moon has already shone twice over the Lupanda-valley since Bonisa's arrival at the Mission Station. When the new moon comes for the third time, MaWanda appears at the hospital one morning.

Jhula sees the woman standing in the shadow of the Mopani trees and recognizes her as Bonisa's mother. Jhula invites her to come into the hospital but she refuses. No, she does not want to go into the white house. She has only come to get her children and after that, she wants to return to Vundla's kraal as quickly as possible.

Somewhat shyly and hesitantly, she follows the nurse across the veranda. The Missionary and Sister Mary come out to greet MaWanda and invite her to come inside, but the woman still refuses and remains silent.

Umfundisi looks with concern at the skinny woman; she seems exhausted. Then he tells her that Bonisa and her little brother are very healthy and happy now. They also ask her to stay at the Mission Post for at least one day.

MaWanda refuses again. She asks for her children and wants them to return with her to their own kraal as soon as possible.

While the Sister leaves to look for the children, Jhula asks MaWanda if Vundla was angry when he heard that she had taken the children to the Mission hospital.

After a long pause MaWanda answers nervously; she whispers to Jhula about her homecoming. On her return trip she had stepped out of the Missionary's car along the bank of the Lupanda river and then she had crossed the river to Limpo-Lupanda, the chief's kraal. There was Tukula, the son of the chief, the one who had advised her to take the children to the Mission Post. It was under his protection that she then returned to her husband's kraal.

Tukula told Vundla that it had been at his command that the children had been taken far South of the Lupandariver, to the house of the white man. Tukula had told Vundla also that he was not to punish or threaten MaWanda. If there were any worries or misfortunes within the family then he would have to go to Tukula's kraal to ask for help or counsel.

While Umfundisi and Sister Mary are in the hospital collecting Bonisa and her little brother, MaWanda shyly asks Jhula if the white people have magically changed the children.

While Jhula is thinking hard about how she must tell MaWanda about Bonisa's change, she sees old MaRunda coming their way. "Ah..." Jhula answers, "MaRunda will tell you about the children."

The two African women sit in front of the hospital in the shade of the Mopani trees. Old MaRunda explains as MaWanda listens attentively. The peace and happiness, which MaRunda speaks about, do not penetrate into MaWanda's heart. In fact, they bring her fear because there is only one thought on MaWanda's mind, Bonisa's amulet has been burnt to ashes! Bonisa no longer asks the amadhlozi for protection. Bonisa prays to Inkosi Jesu, the King of the white man... MaWanda groans softly and her whole body trembles.

Now, Vundla will have yet another reason to be angry. Oh... if her children do not wear and honour the amulet anymore, the spirits will no longer protect them. Perhaps more misfortune will come over the kraal now.

Umfundisi and Sister Mary come on to the veranda with Bonisa and her happy and healthy little brother. MaWanda's mother heart becomes warm and starts to beat faster at the sight of her youngest child. She walks toward the veranda, followed by old MaRunda. She wants to hold her child and talk to him, but the little boy turns away his head and clings to Bonisa. He does not recognize his mother anymore, because they have been at the Mission Post for three months.

This is devastating for MaWanda. Ah... has her youngest child turned against her too?

Then her gaze is drawn toward Bonisa. How beautiful she looks. Sister Rhoda had dressed her in a yellow, cotton dress with white lace around the collar and along the sleeves. A warm glow emanates from her young, dark eyes and a friendly smile spreads across her small, black face as she looks at MaWanda.

"Salibonani," (I see you) says MaWanda.

"Yeeeebo," (Yes, I see you too) answers Bonisa.

"Kunjani?" (How are you keeping?) she continues to ask.

"Sikona," (Very well).

After the customary African greeting, MaWanda wants to leave with the children right away. But the Missionary tries to convince MaWanda to come inside the hospital for a moment since Bonisa must say goodbye to her many friends, young and old, at the Mission Station. However, the woman is afraid and decides to wait outside.

Under the Tshabela tree, in front of the veranda, they stand together for just a short while to say one last goodbye. Bonisa promises Jhula, Amos, and MaRunda that she will not forget the Mission Post and will come back again sometime. Umfundisi and Sister Mary have never before felt so much sadness at the departure of one of their patients.

Bonisa stands in front of the Missionary, her dark eyes glowing warmly and peacefully. They mirror the inner peace and happiness of her young soul. This heathen child of Africa who came to the Lupanda Mission Post as a lost, wandering sheep, has been found by the great Shepherd, through God's grace. He will never allow his sheep to perish.

Just over Bonisa's shoulder, against the backdrop of the woods, Umfundisi sees one white sheep of the flock of the Mission Post. The animal bleats softly. It had become detached from the flock, grazing in the woods and is looking for shelter in its own, familiar surroundings. This picture, of the little girl standing before him with the sheep in the background, moves him deeply. The child must now be separated from her Mission friends and go to the dark North where no flock of Christ has been gathered yet.

Will she be able to confess her Christian faith to her heathen family members? Will she be faithful to her confession of Christ, of whom she had never heard until she had come to the hospital? Will the Lord use this child as a young Missionary to spread the joyful message of the Gospel across the land North of the Lupandariver? There are so many questions in the Missionary's heart to which he has no answer.

They must say goodbye now. For a moment, Bonisa's small black hand lies in the large, white hand of Umfundisi, as he says: "Bonisa, when you are far away from us and feel lonely, when there is no one who understands you, then you can always pray. Ask Nkulu-Nkulu for guidance. He always sees you, even when you are far, far away... He will always listen to you, but you must ask only Him for help and not pray to the spirits of your ancestors. If you ask the amadhlozi for help again, then Inkosi Jesu will be sad and filled with holy anger. Then you will not have His Peace in your soul. You must choose Bonisa. You must pray to Nkulu-Nkulu, the Lord Jehovah, but never again to the spirits. Go to Tukula, the son of the chief, and tell him about the sheep of Inkosi Jesu's flock. Tell him that those sheep will never perish in the darkness of the night. And if they wander off, the Great Shepherd will look for them and bring them back to His flock. He will correct and teach them. They will be with Him forever. Can you recite the text about the sheep once more for me?"

Bonisa folds her hands together, then softly and reverently she says: "*My sheep hear my voice, and they know Me, and they follow Me: and I give unto them eternal life; and they shall never perish.*"

After these words, it remains quiet until Jhula picks up the little boy and places him in the carrier cloth on Bonisa's back. Amos, the African nurse, takes MaWanda and her two children up to the Lupandariver in the hospital jeep.

On the other side of the Lupanda river the trip on foot to Vundla's kraal begins. Soon MaWanda begins to get short of breath and walks more slowly. She is so tired. After crossing another riverbed, she sits on a rock by the riverbank. Bonisa lets her little brother play on the ground for a while. He walks back to the narrow river and splashes with his little hands in the water that flows among the rocks.

MaWanda begins to tell Bonisa about life in the kraal. The corn harvest is small this year and there is not enough sorghum and millet in the storage huts. The dry season is coming, and already the streams are nearly dried up and there is not much grass for the cattle. The boys must take the cattle far North to let the animals drink from a bigger river. Mambi takes care of the sheep now and has never let one sheep get lost.

Bonisa begins to long for the kraal with the sheep, for her brothers and sisters, and her mother's hut.

MaWanda groans softly as they stand up to continue the trip. She puts her hands on her back for support. She is exhausted. The corn harvest has been too much for her weak body. For days on end, she had to carry big baskets, heavily laden with corncobs on her head, from the fields to the kraal. Oh... she is so tired, so very tired.

Fortunately, Bonisa will be home again to help MaWanda, and to get firewood from the forest.

After a few days, Bonisa has adjusted to life in Vundla's kraal again, though everything is different now. Bonisa prays before eating her food and she tells Nkwee, Sikla, and her brothers and sisters about Umfundisi, the white man and MaRunda.

The evenings in MaWanda's hut are wonderful. That is when the women and children of the kraal come to sit around the fire to listen to Bonisa's stories.

Oh, there is so much to tell them. She has memorized the Bible stories about the sheep of Inkosi Jesu very well. There is a childlike happiness in Bonisa when her brothers and sisters listen to her closely.

Nkwee and Sikla whisper together that they would also want to go to the far -away house of the white man. They want to meet Zenja, who once had fire in his eyes but is better now.

MaWanda listens to the stories about Umfundisi's evening services in the hospital. The stories about the heavy burdens of corn baskets, big bundles of firewood, and reedgrass and that Inkosi Jesu says: "Come unto me all ye that labour and are heavy laden and I will give you rest." He can take that heavy burden of sin out of your heart.

MaWanda does not understand Inkosi Jesu, the King of the book of the white man. A king should not carry heavy burdens for his people. The nation must carry the heavy burdens for the king; that is the law of her people. No, MaWanda doesn't understand at all. This makes Bonisa sad.

Oh, it is so difficult to remember everything and to retell it in the right way. The Missionary himself should come to their kraal. He should read to her family from the Holy Book of the Lord Jehovah.

Bonisa longs for the coming of Umfundisi. She longs for the reading from the Bible and the old MaRunda. She wishes she was back again in her own spot in the forest among the Lupandahills where she could pray to the Lord among the high reedgrasss. Though Bonisa is now in Vundla's kraal, far away from the Mission Post, she still often kneels down in a quiet spot in the woods when she is out gathering firewood.

Once, she stayed away for a long time. MaWanda became worried and went out to look for her. She found Bonisa among the thick bushes on her knees, praying to Nkulu-Nkulu.

In the evenings in the hut, Bonisa always kneels beside the fire and prays before she goes to sleep; she prays for MaWanda and for the family; she prays that Inkosi Jesu would send the Missionary to their kraal; she prays for courage to tell Tukula about the Great Shepherd, who always takes care of His sheep, so that they will not perish in the night of eternal darkness.

Although Mambi has to herd the sheep from now on, Bonisa is allowed to go with her. She is a good help for Mambi, especially now that they must sometimes go far into the woods to look for grass and water. Nkwee and Sikla always take the cattle while Mambi and Bonisa follow them at a distance with the sheep.

As the flock lies down to rest in the shade of the Tshabela trees, during the hottest time of the day, Bonisa searches for a Tshekisanebush. She breaks off branches and gathers them in a cloth. In the evening at the kraal, the ends of the brokenoff branches are split and given to the children to brush their teeth. The sap from the branches makes their teeth beautifully white.

Sometimes Bonisa finds a lowgrowing plant with purple soap flowers. She always takes them back to the kraal. MaWanda boils the flowers and the leaves in water and strains the sediment through a grass sieve, leaving her a gourd full of thick, soapy water. She then carries this on her head to the river. There the children have a wonderful time. They laugh loudly while splashing in the river. All the black, frizzy heads are lathered and washed with the soapy water.

When there are no branches for teeth cleaning, or no soap flowers to be found, Bonisa lies down with the flock to sleep, her head next to the sheep. She loves the animals; she calls them by their names and strokes their fleece. Bonisa is a child of the forest. She loves the trees, the birds, the rabbits, and the impala. She loves everything that lives in the forest.

There is much work to be done in the kraal. She must gather firewood; bring water to the kraal, learn which wild vegetables, fruits and seeds are safe to eat and which are poisonous.

Bonisa takes cares of her little brother and learns to crush corn. She shows MaWanda and Mambi which kind of tree roots old MaRunda boils to make dye to color the grass for making baskets. And so, the weeks quickly pass by.

10. THE HONEY GUIDE

Early one morning, Mambi and Bonisa go into the woods again with the flock of sheep. They head South toward the Lupanda valley. They are looking for a new area, where they will find grass for the sheep. The first warm rays of the sun cast a golden glow over the woods on this new day. The impala frolic happily among the trees. The exuberant morning song of the brightly coloured songbirds fills the air.

On their way to the valley, they see how the Limpo-Lupanda kraal glistens in the morning light, high on top of the hill. That is the kraal where Tukula lives.

Bonisa still wants to tell Tukula about the Mission Post and Umfundisi, but her greatest desire is to tell him about Inkosi Jesu. However, she cannot just go to the chief's kraal. It has to be for an important reason, and there isn't one. Therefore, she must wait for an opportunity to speak with Tukula.

As they pass by the forest where Bonisa spent the night looking for her sheep, she shudders. Oh, what a terrifying night that was! Since that night, much has changed in Bonisa's life. She now carries deep in her heart the treasure that she has found; the Great Shepherd, who will never let His sheep perish. His sheep will not be lost forever. She longs to explain this to Tukula.

While the sheep graze in the valley, the girls sit on a rock along the bank of the river. A little bird flies over Bonisa's head. The small animal is chirping excitedly. "She-she-she," it calls. It perches on a branch hanging over the river and calls again: "She-she-she."

The girls pay no attention to it while it flies from the branch and flutters back and forth over their heads, chirping continually. "She-she-she," as if it is calling: "Come with me, come with me!"

The little bird glides over the river, and after a brief pause, the chirping sounds again, even more pressing: "She-she-she." Now it flies right in front of them, calling repeatedly: "She-she-she."

Suddenly Mambi calls out: "Oh, come! It's a honey guide!" She jumps up and shouts to the little bird: "Yes, I'm coming!"

The little bird notices that the girls follow it. This makes him happy, and with its wings, spread out widely, it sings a song of joy.

"You go with him. Follow him wherever he leads you," Mambi commands her younger sister. "I will go and call Nkwee for help. Go quickly. The bird is getting impatient. Follow it to the tree where there must be a bees' nest."

Bonisa is very excited. A honey guide has chosen her to find the honey tree. What a feast! She calls: "Yes, I'm coming!" She watches closely to see where the honey guide is going. The little brown bird sees that the child is following and flies, chirping joyfully, to a tree thirty meters ahead. It swoops down on the lowest branch, looks at Bonisa and keeps on singing happily: "She-she-she."

The bird continues to fly a few more meters then rests for a moment on a low branch. It looks inquisitively at Bonisa, wondering whether she is following and whistles happily when it sees that she is coming. It guides her through the woods. Again and again the little bird flies ahead and each time it waits for a moment to see if she is still following, while constantly chirping, "She-she-she."

Finally, after nearly half a mile, it settles quietly on the branch of a big baobab tree. Now the bird's call has changed into an excited trill. It flutters from branch to branch, continuously shooting down in front of a small opening in the hollow of the tree.

Bonisa understands clearly that a little girl like herself cannot get the honey out alone; she must get help somewhere, and soon, otherwise the little bird will find someone else to get the honey. Whom should she call? Nkwee is too far away.

Suddenly she has an idea: Tukula! She must go and fetch Tukula. This will be his reward for protecting her from her angry father, after the sheep had been killed by wild animals. She calls to the little bird: "Wait, I'll be back!"

As fast as she can, she runs through the woods along the narrow trail to the Limpo-kraal. Halfway up the hill to the high kraal of the chief, a boy stands on guard. He forbids Bonisa to go any further.

Bonisa explains to him that she has an important message for the son of the chief. A tiny, mocking smirk begins to form on the boy's black face. Then he whistles a few high notes, upon which a second guard comes down the path. This boy has to take the place of the first guard. The guard walks up the steep path to announce to the kraalhead that there is a visitor.

Not long afterwards, the headman of the chief, followed by Tukula, comes walking solemnly down the steep path.

Bonisa kneels to the ground. She feels a deep respect for Tukula; his kingly appearance and the fierce, penetrating look in his eyes, makes her shy. For a while no words are exchanged. The girl doesn't dare to move and remains kneeling down in front of Tukula.

When the headman asks her why she has come to the Limpo kraal, she whispers timidly: "It's in the forest."

Tukula commands his headman to return to the kraal. He will go himself with the girl into the woods.

The little honey guide that won't rest until the honey hole is opened, has followed Bonisa on her way to the kraal. It is flying over her head again, all the while trilling impatiently: "She-she-she."

"The honey guide," she says to Tukula. "He called me. Now I'm calling you to get the honey."

"Why don't you call Vundla or your brothers? Wouldn't they be happy to find the honey tree?"

For a moment, Bonisa is quiet. Then she answers shyly: "Because Tukula protected me and brought me home after the sheep were killed."

Silently, they follow the little bird that has resumed its whistling.

105

Again he flutters from tree to tree, leading the way, until he comes to rest by the big Baobab tree. Like an arrow, it darts past the opening of the hollow tree trunk.

"Ah..." says Tukula, "There is the honey."

When the honey guide notices that its followers have come to a standstill at the massive tree trunk and that they have spotted the honey, its tune changes to a beautiful song of joy. Tukula and Bonisa listen in awe.

The little creature flies to a lower branch, proudly ruffles its feathers, spreads out its wings, and expectantly cocks its head to one side in the direction of the bees' nest, waiting for its reward of bee larvae and wax comb.

Tukula, who knows all the secrets of life in the forest, now goes to work with calm determination. He examines a long split in the tree trunk, where lightning may have struck many years ago. There must be a hollow space behind the split, where the bees have built their nest. Bonisa sees many bees, busily flying in and out of the opening. Now she must get handfuls of dry grass.

Tukula prepares a fire and uses the grass that Bonisa has picked to produce a lot of smoke. They squat next to the fire. Bonisa has to help Tukula to blow the smoke into the hole of the trunk.

When the smoke inside the hollow tree rises, they hear the loud and angry buzzing of bees, but soon this changes into a softer sound. Tukula explains that the bees are now filling their tummies with as much honey as possible and will not be so ready to sting.

As soon as the buzzing is softer, he climbs up the tree with a basket on his back. He enlarges the opening in the trunk, so that he can get at the honey. Tukula puts pieces of beautiful comb, filled with honey in his basket and slides down the trunk, while the rich, sweet honey is dripping from his hands.

The little bird can no longer hide its eagerness when he sees the honey comb in front of him. It chirps excitedly and flutters around them.

"Have patience, little friend," says Tukula, "Your reward is coming."

Again, he climbs into the tree and returns with a piece of comb filled with white, glistening bee larvae. The honey guide is happy when it sees the reward.

Mambi, Nkwee, and Sikla walk over and squat down beside Tukula. Tukula explains to Bonisa, that some of the bee larvae and wax must always be given to the honey guide. "Look," he says, "You must always leave some of the comb with bee-grubs on a piece of bark or on a large leaf in the shade of a bush on the ground. That way the hot sun cannot dry it out. It stays fresh longer in the shade. Our little friend, the honey guide, eats very little at a time because his crop is small. He will have a feast for several days. We will take the big pieces of honey comb home, but first you can have a taste of it."

Tukula breaks off a piece of comb for everyone. The children sit on the ground while Tukula finds a spot on a fallen tree trunk. So, on this sunny morning, they have an unexpected feast of good, sweet honey and nourishing, fresh bee larvae.

Tukula tells Vundla's children the story of a boy who was once called by a honey guide. Happily, the boy followed the little bird. When he came to the honey nest, he ate some of it himself and took the rest with him to the kraal, but he didn't leave a reward for the honey guide that had called him. Out of selfishness, just to have everything to himself, he did not leave anything for the eager, little honey guide. However, the bird followed the boy home to find out where he lived.

One afternoon, sometime later, the little guide flew to the kraal of the young cowherd. It whistled and called: "She-she-she."

"Ah..." the boy thought, "there is the honey guide! It is calling me again. Now, I will get more of that good honey. What a feast!"

The boy followed the bird that constantly called to him: "She-

she-she," beckoning him deep into the forest.

Finally the honey guide came to rest on a low branch of a tree, spread his little wings and sang a joyful song, as if it was saying: "Here we are at the honey tree".

Indeed, there was a hollow trunk; the boy squatted, looked into the hole and... for a moment, Tukula's eyes flicker brightly as he looks at the children one by one. Then he continues in a low voice: "And then... a big mamba snake slithered out of the hole and bit the boy's leg. Several hours later, the young cowherd died from the poisonous snakebite. That was his punishment for being selfish and not giving the honey guide its rightlydeserved reward.

And now, you children of Vundla, never forget to reward the honey guide, otherwise he will punish you."

As Tukula gets up to go back to his own kraal, Bonisa stands in front of him. Her dark, childish eyes look at him in earnest, as she says: "If we don't wear an amulet anymore, but still ask the amadhlozi for help, Nkulu-Nkulu will punish us."

Alarmed, Mambi shouts: "Oh... don't say that...! Oh, the amadhlozi will punish us!"

Sikla jumps up, and as he clenches his fists in front of Bonisa, he says to Tukula: "She has been in the house of the white man and now she doesn't want to wear an amulet for protection anymore! But, father Vundla will send her out of the kraal if she keeps refusing to wear one. He will have the medicine man come."

"Inkosi Jesu is more powerful than the medicine man," Bonisa says softly, "and Inkosi Jesu is the Great Shepherd; His sheep will never perish."

Never before did Tukula, the son of the chief of the Lupanda-district, see such a calm, peaceful glow in the eyes of a child of his tribe as he now sees in Bonisa's eyes.

She says to him: "If Tukula also becomes a sheep of Inkosi Jesu, he will never be lost in the dark night. I always pray to Inkosi Jesu... for Tukula... I don't pray to the amadhlozi anymore, only to Nkulu-

Nkulu. That's what the Holy Book of Umfundisi tells us to do."

Sikla, Mambi, and Nkwee are becoming impatient. Ah... why does Bonisa have to tell again about the Book of that Umfundisi on this beautiful morning? They look timidly at Tukula to see if he is angry.

Tukula orders them to continue into the woods with the flock, but Bonisa must stay with him and tell him everything about the Mission hospital and the Book of the white man.

11. THE DOWRY

The cool, dry season has passed. Not a drop of rain has fallen for months. Now that the new rainy season is drawing near, a lot of hard work is being done in the fields. The rough earth is plowed; the corn and sorghum are sown. Everything is waiting for the much-needed rain. Each morning the Africans look up at the clear, blue sky with great expectation. Their eyes scan the bright, blue skies to see if there is even a small rain-cloud to be seen anywhere; but there isn't one.

Disappointed and filled with fear, the kraalheads gather for a meeting. Vundla is also present. A heathen priest leads the meeting. The men discuss what they must do to please the amadhlozi in order that the spirits of the ancestors will send rain.

The priest throws some magic bones on the ground, studies the criss-cross pattern in which the little bones are displayed, and finds the answer. The amadhlozi want to receive a great offering. After that, the spirits will send rain. Out of every kraal, a cow or goat must be brought to the priest. He will offer several animals, and the ones that are left over he will keep as his payment.

With much care, Vundla picks a nice goat from his herd. A cow is too costly an offer for him. He is already missing three beautiful sheep and soon MaWanda's father will come for the rest of the wedding dowry. Three cows, or... MaWanda's eldest daughter, Mambi.

The evening of the offering ceremony has arrived. In the kraals, the women and girls have everything well-prepared. A lot of beer has been brewed, and they will eat a delicacy: black caterpillars. The children had gathered them in the forest in the rainy season and then dried them in the sun. Now they are soaked and cooked. Beautifully woven baskets filled with black caterpillars and roasted peanuts are ready for the feast.

Families from afar have been invited to come and celebrate the ancient, heathen rain ceremony a feast to honour the spirits, so that they will send rain.

Nkwee, Sikla, Mambi and the little brothers and sisters are excited about the feast. But Vundla and MaWanda are not happy. They are very worried and afraid that the spirits will not send rain on their corn and millet fields because... Bonisa refuses to celebrate the feast with them.

Bonisa is sitting in MaWanda's hut; she is praying to Inkosi Jesu that she will remain obedient to His commandment. She does not want to participate in the spirit worship.

While Bonisa stays in the hut alone, Vundla's family gathers with all the visitors around a big fire, in the center of the kraal.

The heathen priest has a place of honour. The kraalhead, Vundla, makes a short speech. The priest then walks slowly and reverently toward the spirit-tree. Everyone follows the priest. They bow and kneel in front of the tree. This is a sign for the spirits of the ancestors, who are looking down on them from the tree, that their descendants honour them and plead for their favour. The heathen priest offers the goat and prays to the amadhlozi not to send misfortune, but to be merciful to them by soon sending rain on the dry fields.

Following the priest's prayer, the feasting begins. The men share a big calabash of homemade beer; the women drink too and eat the cooked, black caterpillars and the nuts, along with the children.

After the meal, the children must dance around the spirit tree. They sing and clap their hands to the rhythm of the drums. The eyes of Nkwee sparkle; the priest has appointed him to beat the drum.

It soon becomes night. In the woods, the dark branches of the trees appear like black silhouettes against the sky. The clear, bright moon shines its cool silver beams down through the many treetops, swaying slowly in the wind.

Upon a signal from the priest, the hands beat the drums more quickly. The monotone drone changes into a fiercer rhythm. Faster and faster, the hands move over the drum, and the bonechilling tempo of the drum echoes through the silent night.

The people at the woodfire stand up, form a ring around the spirit-tree, and dance to the beat of the drum. The women sing; the men holler; the children clap their hands, and the music drones on, sounding ominous and wild. Faster and louder, the drum beats; faster and wilder, the people dance. They stare at the spirit tree, at the invisible spirits of their ancestors. The amadhlozi must be pleased by this pagan evening celebration, held in their honour. The spirits should send rain now.

The drumming, drinking of beer, the singing and dancing, goes on for hours until everyone is exhausted and stumbles into the huts to sleep.

Bonisa cannot sleep. Oh, she knows that father Vundla and the entire family are very angry with her. A struggle begins in her heart. Is it really true that the Lord Jesus, the Son of God, is dishonored by the worship of the spirits of the ancestors? Yes, it says so in the Holy Book, the Bible, and Umfundisi has read about it.

Bonisa longs for Umfundisi and the old MaRunda. There are still so many things that she doesn't understand and would like to ask them; that's why she prays that the Lord will send a Missionary to their kraal to tell her family about the Bible and Inkosi Jesu.

The next morning there is a mess in the usually tidy kraal. When the drunken people retired to their huts the night before, nothing was cleaned up and the women had not swept the kraal ground.

Vundla wakes up in an irritable and angry mood. What will he do with Bonisa, that disobedient child? He would very much like to whip her, as he used to do, to punish his children, but Tukula does not allow that anymore. He had submitted himself to Tukula and handed over his whip. What punishment can he now use for this wayward child?

With angry, impatient strides, he paces up and down in front of his hut. MaMoyo, his eldest wife, comes over to him and listens to his angry words. "Ah..." he cries heatedly, "what does it mean when an eight-year-old child comes back to our family with new ideas from the white people and says that a beerfeast is wrong and sinful? And that the God of the white people will be angry with her if she takes part?"

Vundla speaks with a furious voice... But suddenly the tone of his voice changes and an expression of fear comes over his face as he says: "Oh... I fear that the amadhlozi will punish all of us, oh... what will happen to us?"

Tremors of fear distort his face as he continues in a hoarse voice: "This is the first time that someone from our family has refused to celebrate such a feast with us. Our parents have celebrated it and our grandparents have celebrated it, yes, all the forefathers of our tribe. And now, suddenly, a child, a girl of eight years old, tells us that God forbids this. Oh... this is terrible! She will bring the wrath of all our ancestor spirits over this family, because she has refused to honour them."

Fear of the spirits' punishment overwhelms Vundla. He decides to go to Tukula for advice on how he can make his unwilling daughter obedient.

In the Limpo-Lupanda kraal, Tukula tries to calm the upset and frightened Vundla. He promises Vundla that he will go to the Lupanda Mission Post to ask the white man why Bonisa is forbidden to celebrate the rain ceremony.

When Vundla departs from the chief's kraal, he is calm again, but his thoughts are dark. He is afraid of more misfortune.

Upon his return to the kraal, he sees a visitor sitting in front of his hut. A shock goes through him when he recognizes the visitor. It is Dodo, MaWanda's father. He has come for payment of the dowry. There has been a corn harvest twelve times now since MaWanda became his wife. Now everything has to be paid off.

Vundla feels his entire body shake. Three cows are too costly a gift as payment for such a weak woman as MaWanda. She cannot work hard and she hasn't brought him much fortune in all the years that she has been living in the kraal. No, he will not pay the three cows; MaWanda is definitely not worth it.

After the customary African greeting Vundla takes Grandfather Dodo into his hut to discuss what the dowry payment should be in order to satisfy both of them.

MaWanda is at work in her hut. She sits by the woodfire. She is weaving a sleeping mat, while Bonisa sits beside her and rolls tree bark fibers between her hands to twist string for the mat. MaWanda is afraid of Vundla's temper. Each moment she fears that he will call her and beat her because Bonisa has been so unwilling. Bonisa is her daughter. She has to make sure that from now on the girl will celebrate all the drinking feasts.

In Bonisa's heart is such a wonderful peace and calm. The love of Inkosi Jesu is stronger than her fear of the angry Vundla. She has just asked the Lord if he will send the Missionary to the kraal. She has prayed for her mother and her little brother and for all who live in their kraal and... for Tukula. And MaWanda listened.

The discussion between Grandfather Dodo and Vundla takes several hours. Two of Vundla's brothers, who stayed in the kraal after the rain feast, are present at the meeting as witnesses. Vundla must choose what he wants to pay: three beautiful cows, or MaWanda's eldest daughter Mambi.

He doesn't want to give up three cows. And Mambi...? Mambi, who is so good at herding the sheep? She has never let any sheep wander away as Bonisa did. No, he does not want to give Mambi away either.

Suddenly Vundla knows what he will do. Not the cows, not Mambi, but... Bonisa, she can be used to settle the dowry. What a wonderful plan! Vundla begins to sum up all of Bonisa's valuable qualities to his father-in-law, Dodo. She is strong; she can carry heavy loads of firewood and reedgrass. She can carry big gourds with water on her head, without spilling one drop. She is skilled in twisting rope, weaving mats and many other things. "And," says Vundla with emphasis, "on the other side of the big Shandingu-river, she will probably forget about her Inkosi Jesu."

For a moment, it remains quiet in the hut. The men look into the fire without saying anything. Vundla's brothers who had seen Bonisa refuse to celebrate the feast for the amadhlozi, nod in agreement. The eldest brother who lives far to the South, close to the Zendigho Mission Post, says: "The spirit of Inkosi Jesu, that great medicine man, is so powerful, that all the witchdoctors in Africa can't drive him away."

After a short silence Dodo answers: "Ah, who is this Inkosi Jesu? We have our own medicine men. Jesus does not live in our land, on the other side of the Shandingu-river. With us lives the 'great Mazenga', the best medicine man!"

MaWanda and Bonisa are called to prepare the meal for grandfather Dodo and the other men.

With a sharp eye grandfather follows every move of the girl. "She does do her work well", he thinks. "She is still young, but after a few years, she will surely be worth seven cows. And in those years she can work in the fields for MaWanda's mother, the old Ugogo."

MaWanda and her child are in their own hut again. Now, Dodo lets Vundla know that he accepts Bonisa as payment for the dowry instead of the three cows. The girl will have to work hard to show that she really is of the same value as three beautiful cows.

With dismay, MaWanda and her child listen to Vundla's words as

116

he tells them that Bonisa must go with grandfather Dodo. MaWanda groans. She puts her hands in front of her eyes and Bonisa clings fast to her mother. No, she doesn't want to...! She wants to stay with her mother.

The rest of the family and the little brothers and sisters join them. MaWanda is crying, and with her head bowed she goes into the hut to put together Bonisa's few possessions.

Grandfather is in a hurry. He wants to leave immediately, because from Vundla's kraal it is many hours of walking to reach the river. Before the moon goes down, they must wade through the great Shandingu-river, in its bright light.

Bonisa is so shocked by her father's sudden decision that it is hard for her to think clearly. MaWanda comes out of the hut again; she is holding a rolled up sleeping mat and a hide blanket, a wooden spoon and a corn basket for Bonisa.

The deeply saddened woman stands still in the opening of the hut and begins to sob loudly. Bonisa holds tightly onto her mom and cries out: "I'm coming back, Mother! I will come back! I will pray to the Lord. He will bring me back to you!"

With a rough tug Vundla pulls her away from MaWanda. "You! Come back...?" he snaps. "You will never live in this kraal or in this land again. Go with your grandfather, now!"

It is a sad goodbye. MaWanda cries and her little brother holds out his hands to Bonisa and calls: "Nisa... Nisa..."

"Mother," Bonisa whispers softly, "Mother, you must pray every night in your hut for Umfundisi to come."

At the entrance of the kraal, the women and children watch the grandfather and his granddaughter go. "This is Bonisa's punishment," they think, "because she didn't want to kneel to the spirit tree."

With long strides, grandfather walks along the forest path and Bonisa has to follow him. Ah, everything happened so suddenly;

117

she hadn't even been able to say goodbye to Nkwee, Sikla and Mambi. They were still with the herd in the woods.

But why does she have to go to the distant kraal of Dodo? Isn't Mambi the eldest daughter? She has prayed so much for Umfundisi to come to their kraal, and now she has to go far away. Bonisa doesn't understand it at all.

For the first while, they walk over familiar forest ground; she has been here many times with the cattle and sheep. After walking for several hours, twilight falls over the woods and a strong wind causes the tree branches to creak. Bonisa begins to feel ever so lonely.

Shacombe is the most Northern kraal in the Lupanda valley; Bonisa has been there once before. One of father's brothers lives there. Grandfather Dodo goes into the kraal for a short visit, to get some food and to bring greetings from the Vundla family.

12. TO THE OTHER SIDE OF THE GREAT RIVER

From Shacombe they walk through an entirely different forest. There are fewer shrubs here and different trees. Bright moonlight shines through the woods and lights up the trunks of teak and mahogany trees. The wind rushes through the treetops, fiercely whipping them back and forth; the branches groan and creak. The long, dark shadows of the swaying trees move across the ground and it looks as though countless dark creatures scurry along the forest floor in the direction of the river.

There are no more trees ahead of them. The full moonlight shines on the river and over the reedgrass along the shore. The forest track also ends. Only a very narrow footpath continues through the rustling, waving reeds. The grass is so tall that Bonisa cannot see anything anymore, only the yellow-green reed-stalks with their brown plumes on top. It sounds as though the reedgrass is singing.

The dark plumes are like many dark hands that wave a farewell, as she travels to the distant kraal; so far away on the other side of the great Shandingu-river!

Just before the river, Grandfather comes to a halt. He shields his eyes with his hand and peers sharply out over the swirling water of the river. He studies the bend in the river where the thorn trees spread out their long branches and under those branches are the cool, dark shelters for the crocodiles.

"Look there," grandfather says, and points with his hand across the river, "That is the crocodile bend; it is very dangerous there. We can't see the crocodiles, but they can see us. They lie in wait for anyone that comes through the river. They hide in their dark shelters under the thorn tree branches. We will ask the amadhlozi for protection: Amadhlozi, spirits of our ancestors, we ask you for protection; we will always honour you," Grandfather speaks out, as

119

he looks upon the girl who stands next to him, so small and scared.

Bonisa stands completely still. Her lips are tightly shut; her small hands are clasped and she says nothing.

When not a single word comes out of her mouth, the old African leans over to her. He lays his big, heavy hand on her head.

Bonisa stands beside him filled with fear. The water of the river rushes and swirls along the shore and splashes over their feet and on their legs. In the bend of the river, the current beats around the tree trunks that grow out of the water and chases along the shore. The reedgrass stalks bow even lower.

"Listen carefully," says Grandfather, "the reedgrass sings for the amadhlozi, for the spirits that live in this river. Look and see how the reedgrass bows to the spirits to honour them. They are the spirits of the river that must protect us on our trip to the other shore. Therefore, we bow for them as well."

The big, bony hand of grandfather presses heavily on Bonisa's head and his voice is stern, making her increasingly afraid.

Slowly and solemnly, he utters the words: "Amadhlozi, we ask you for your protection. We will always honour you."

Then the African takes a deep bow among the waving reedgrass. His hand still rests on Bonisa's head as he presses her down. Her knees bend and her head bows, but she remains silent.

Grandfather's voice bellows above the sound of the rushing water: "Ah, don't you want to talk? Then, I will teach you. Repeat after me."

He takes his hand from her head and roughly grips her shoulder.

Bonisa stands upright again, among the singing reeds.

Once more, the man repeats his prayer to the spirits, and Bonisa, who could scream because of the pain in her shoulder, softly repeats his words. "Amadhlozi, we ask you for protection."

Grandfather releases her shoulder. Her legs tremble, and tears well up in her eyes, but she doesn't want to cry. No, she wants to be brave.

"Come," says the man, "we are going to wade through the river now. Hold tightly onto this club and walk closely behind me. I know where the stones are over which we can cross. Watch carefully where I put my feet. Follow exactly my every footstep."

With his left hand he holds tightly onto the club and with his right hand he clutches a sharp, pointed spear. If the crocodiles come near, he will either overpower them with one thrust of his spear, or defend himself with the club in his hand.

Bonisa grips the thick end of the club with both hands and follows Grandfather to where the reedgrass stops. The swift-moving Shandingu-river now lies before them. The silver beams of the moon dance and shimmer on the rippling water.

Yet again, Grandfather looks with the sharp gaze of a hunter in all directions to see if there is any danger. Then he goes on, into the water. Bonisa walks behind him. At first slowly and then with greater speed she follows him, jumping from one stone to the next.

The reedgrass continues to sing, as their dark plumes, like many dark hands, wave a sad goodbye.

She looks behind her once more. Oh, how she would like to raise both hands to wave goodbye to the land of her birth. She thinks of the people whom she will never see again; the people with whom she can never speak again. Her mother, and all her sisters and brothers, and the sheep... and Tukula, and the Missionary and... Inkosi Jesu.

Suddenly, tears well up in her eyes and roll down her cheeks; she cries. Deep in her heart a desperate voice is calling: "No, no! I don't want to...! Inkosi Jesu...! I don't dare to go alone with Grandfather. I am so afraid!"

Bonisa sobs. She can no longer hide her sadness, and through her tears she can barely see the stones on which to place her feet.

"Watch your step" Grandfather grumbles angrily. "You might fall into the river and the crocodiles will take you."

She tries to pay more attention; she must not slide off the rocks.

In the middle of the river is a sandbank where the stones can be seen above the water. There they stand still and look around to see whether there are any crocodiles on the northern banks.

Bonisa's heart pounds wildly, but grandfather does not wait long. They must carry on quickly because their destination is still far away. The river is becoming deep again. Bonisa grips the club tightly. The water comes up to her waist so grandfather now has to use all his strength to pull her forward. The current almost drags her off the stones.

The river is wide and it takes a long time before they finally reach the other side of the great Shandingu-river.

The Northern shore is high and steep. Bonisa is so tired that she has no strength left to climb up. She lets herself be pulled along by Grandfather who clambers onto the shore, then grabs onto a low-hanging branch and pulls himself up.

A moment later they stand on the high shore of the river under the trees. There, Bonisa lets go of the club. Now she can just walk behind grandfather; she must follow him, wherever he goes.

Grandfather stares across the river that is now far below them. It looks like a stream of silver in the moonlight.

Bonisa looks worriedly at her grandfather. What will he do now?

"Look," he says, pointing his arm in the direction of the river.

Bonisa stands beside him and listens.

"Look," repeats Grandfather, while he points beyond river. "There, on the other side of the great river, is the kraal where you used to live. That is where Vundla lives, the husband of my daughter, MaWanda. You will not live in her hut anymore. You must forget the kraal of Vundla and MaWanda and your friends and your sheep. You will live in a new land, in a new kraal with Ugogo and my family. You must forget that land on the other side of the great river. The amadhlozi have protected us on our journey through the river. We will honour them."

He puts his arm down again, lays his hand on the girl's shoulder and says: "Bow for the amadhlozi."

The strong pressure of his hand forces Bonisa to the ground and she bows... Grandfather bows too and thanks the spirits for their protection. Bonisa must repeat it; she doesn't dare to refuse, so she softly whispers the words after Grandfather.

They have only walked a short distance through the forest when grandfather stops in front of a round hut. He makes a coughing sound, then waits several minutes. But, no one responds. Not a single sound is heard. Grandfather goes inside. Bonisa follows. She squats on the ground and puts her few belongings beside her.

Grandfather makes a fire with some branches, found inside. Then they sit quietly by the fire. She is exhausted. The warmth of the flames makes Bonisa sleepy and soon her head begins to nod. A little while later she lies down on the ground, wraps herself in her antelope hide and falls asleep.

Grandfather remains seated by the fire for a long time and thinks; he is satisfied about his trip to the North; he has received a good payment for the dowry of MaWanda. Vundla had yet to pay him three cows, but this young girl, MaWanda's daughter, will be worth seven cows in a few years time. In the years that lie ahead, she can work in his kraal and carry water from the river and get wood from the forest for old Ugogo. Yes, he got a bargain.

After several hours of deep sleep Bonisa awakes and looks around, bewildered. Next to her smolders a woodfire. But, she doesn't see her mother; she doesn't hear the cheerful voice of her little brother calling, "Nisa... nisa..." to wake her up, because he wants to play with her first thing in the morning.

Slowly the memory of the previous day comes back. Oh... now she remembers. She is not at home, in the hut with her mother anymore. They crossed that dreadful river last night, and now she is in the new land.

Bonisa's heart fills with sadness again. She is in the new land.

The land where Inkosi Jesu does not live...

But she doesn't want to live in a land where He does not live! She wants to go back... back to the other side of the great river. She wants to go back to the land where Umfundisi lives; she wants to go back to the white hospital where they sing so beautifully about Nkulu-Nkulu. No, she doesn't want to stay here!

It is quiet in the hut. Grandfather is not there. Maybe he is in the woods, looking for wild roots or fruits to eat.

The dark night has passed. Bonisa sees the first rays of this new day shine through the trees as she peers through the narrow cracks of the hut. She feels so abandoned and alone in this new land!

In her thoughts, she hears the voice of Umfundisi again when he said to her in the hospital: "Bonisa, when you are sad and lonely, and there is no one to help you, then you must pray and ask the Lord to help you. He always sees you; He always hears you, but you must ask Him alone for help, not the spirits of your ancestors anymore. If you ask the amadhlozi for help, then Inkosi Jesu will be sad, and also full of anger. You must choose Bonisa. You must pray to the Lord, but never again to the spirits."

Umfundisi's words come from deep within her memory. She crawls out from beneath the hide and kneels down beside the woodfire. She folds her hands together and wants to pray. In her heart there is such a great longing for the Lord. This longing is much stronger than that for her own mother and the family back in her land.

Grandfather has said that she must forget everything about the land on the other side of the river, but that is not possible. How can she ever forget that Inkosi Jesu had become her King, while she lived in the other land?

Bonisa wants to pray but she thinks about the evening before when they stood among the reedgrass at the river and grandfather had told her to ask the amadhlozi for protection. Oh, she didn't want to. She had promised the Lord that she would never ask the spirits for help again.

But she had done it anyway. She was so afraid of Grandfather and the current of the river and the crocodiles! Would the Lord want to help her now? Maybe Inkosi Jesu does not want to be her King anymore; she is afraid that He is watching her now as Umfundisi had said.

Bonisa covers her face with her hands and weeps with overwhelming sadness. She cries because she is so alone, and yet... yet in her heart there is that great longing... a longing for Him whom she will never be able to forget.

She doesn't dare to pray, but deep in her sad heart a voice calls: "Inkosi Jesu, I could never forget You. And if You are angry with me, if You don't want to be my King anymore, then I will still always love You... Always."

She leaves the hut to look for Grandfather. It is still quiet in the forest, except for the birds that happily sing their morning song. The Impala frolic lithely among the trees. They are looking for the forest path that leads down to the river.

Oh, she wants to go back, back to her own land and to Umfundisi, to tell him that she has prayed to the amadhlozi again. She also wants to tell him that Inkosi Jesu won't help her anymore.

It is just a short distance from the hut to the river. She cannot see the water through the thick brush, but she can hear its current rush by. She cuts her legs on a thorn bush and a small trickle of blood runs down her skin. Nevertheless, she presses onward through the brush until, suddenly, the wide river lies before her.

Oh, there is so much water! The night they walked through it, she had not realized that the river was so wide! And there on the other side, far behind the dark woods, is her land, where Inkosi Jesu lives. She can never flee back through the river. She knows that she must live in this new land alone, the land of the spirits.

For one last time, she looks across the water. She sees the waving stalks of reeds with their brown plumes, waving their last goodbye.

Again she weaves her way through the brush and heads back to the hut. Maybe Grandfather will be angry that she walked off. But it is still quiet inside the hut; no one is there.

The woodfire is barely smoldering now; it must burn somewhat better before Grandfather returns. Carefully she rakes some ashes out of the glowing embers and shoves a few new and dry twigs on the fire. Quite quickly, the dry wood begins to crackle and catch fire, and soon little red flames appear.

Bonisa unrolls her sleeping mat and sits down beside the fire. She will wait until Grandfather comes back. She crosses her legs, leans her elbows on her knees, and rests her head in her hands. So, she continues to stare into the red flames.

It is very quiet in the hut, and in this stillness, the memory of the Mission hospital comes vividly back into her thoughts, as if she was there again. She remembers that one evening when they all sat under the trees behind the hospital. The women had made a fire and many patients had come to sit around it. Umfundisi had come to sit with them on the ground. He had spoken about the Great King who is the Good Shepherd of His sheep. Ah... how friendly the eyes of the white man were! And how beautiful his voice when he talked about Inkosi Jesu, the Good Shepherd, who never leaves his sheep alone. When one lamb wanders so far away that nobody can find it, and when no one hears the frightened bleating of that lonely sheep, the Great Shepherd will hear it. He looks for the sheep, He calls it, and the sheep hears His voice.

Umfundisi had the holy book of Nkulu-Nkulu in his hands. The book was open and he had read from it the words that Inkosi Jesu himself had spoken: "I am the Good Shepherd, my sheep hear my voice, and I know them, and they follow me."

Then they were all allowed to repeat the words out of the holy book and they had whispered softly: "I am the Good Shepherd, my sheep hear my voice, and I know them, and they follow me."

Oh, it had been so quiet and peaceful there, at the back of the hospital and then she, Bonisa, had wept. It had been as though it was no longer the voice of Umfundisi who read the words, but another voice, so powerful and kind, that she had heard in her heart. A voice that spoke: "I am the Good Shepherd, my sheep hear my voice." Then she believed that it could only be the voice of Inkosi Jesu himself.

The women had looked at her angrily and whispered that she was too young to listen, that she should go to her hut to sleep. But she had remained seated by the warm fire and listened intently. Each word of the Missionary had penetrated deep into her heart. She wasn't afraid of the spirits any longer then, because she had believed that the Lord Jesus was much stronger than all the evil spirits.

Then, when all the women and children had gone back inside the hospital and to the huts to sleep, old MaRunda had stayed by the fire with Bonisa. She had told MaRunda that in her heart was such a love for Inkosi Jesu. And the old woman had said: "You are still young, Bonisa. There are so many wise words in the holy book of Nkulu-Nkulu. You still have to learn them all. The Lord also says: 'If you love me, keep my commandments'. Ah... then you will know whether you really love Him. You will want to be obedient to his commandments, not because you are afraid of Him, the Great King, but because you love Him."

Bonisa is sad now. She feels like a little lamb that has been taken away from the land where the Lord had found her. But the faithful Shepherd, who never lets his sheep perish in sadness and loneliness, puts faith into the child's heart. She believes that He will still take care of her.

A warm glow of love and trust fills her sad heart when she hears again that powerful voice say the words: "My sheep hear my voice and they follow me." Joy fills her soul. She kneels down beside the fire and says aloud: "Inkosi Jesu, will You still speak to me? I have been so disobedient. I asked the amadhlozi for protection in the river. Inkosi Jesu, are You really going with me into this new land? Because I heard Your voice again. Will You forgive my disobedience and cleanse my heart from sin? Help me, Lord, to be obedient to Your commandments because I always want to love You."

There is some shuffling just outside the entrance of the hut. The old African, who has returned from his early walk through the woods, comes in to see if his granddaughter is awake. Shocked, he stares at the kneeling girl whose hands are clasped and whose head is bowed forward. Had he heard it aright? Was she talking to someone, when he came into the hut?

"Ah..." he says, "You are awake and talking to the fire."

"Ah..." she answers timidly, "I'm awake and I'm praying to Inkosi Jesu."

"Ah... ah," he says as he holds up both hands to stop her. "No, He doesn't live here in our land. But, I see that you have the fire burning, that's good, that's good. I have brought some food along; it has to be roasted. Your mother, MaWanda, was good at roasting corn. Let me see if you have learned that from her."

Bonisa stands up straightaway, bows slightly for Grandfather and takes the corncobs from him. She kneels by the fire and turns the cobs slowly in the flames. If the kernels snap too quickly, the cobs have to be put aside to cool a little and then rotated in the heat of the fire again. A delicious aroma spreads throughout the hut.

Bonisa realizes that her stomach is empty and craves for the corncob from which yellow fat droplets glow on the kernels. She lays both cobs on a few dry corn leaves and squats in front of Grandfather. She offers him the biggest cob. He eats it hungrily.

Bonisa sits on her sleeping mat, takes the other cob in her hands to eat it, but then puts it down again. Her fear of Grandfather returns for just a moment, but then suddenly she folds her hands together, looks calmly at him and says: "When I get food, I always pray to Inkosi Jesu for a blessing. Umfundisi taught me that and I will continue to do so in this new land."

Immediately she shuts her eyes and prays aloud: "Lord, will You bless this food and I thank You that You protected us from the crocodiles and the strong current in the river. Will You protect us on the trip to Ugogo. Amen."

There is peace in her heart now. She looks at Grandfather and says: "I have learned beautiful songs about Nkulu-Nkulu. I will sing them for Ugogo when I meet her and I will tell her about the holy book of Jehovah."

"Ah..." grandfather snarls, "you've come to work for Ugogo, not to bring new customs into our land. And we ask the amadhlozi for protection. Eat your corn because the journey is still long."

When Grandfather has finished eating, he stands in the opening of the hut and looks impatiently at the girl, who has finished her corn, but she remains seated. He sees that she has again folded her hands. He hears her say: "Lord, I thank You for the food and will You give Grandfather a new heart so that he too can be a sheep of Your flock? Grandfather is old... but surely You will also have old sheep. Amen."

Anger flares up in Grandfather. He picks up a piece of wood and throws it into the hut; it lands in the middle of the fire and sends some small, burning twigs flying up into the air that almost land on Bonisa's bare feet.

Shocked, she jumps aside and sees how Grandfather threatens her with his fist. "Lord, help me," she sighs.

Fortunately, the old man goes outside. He does not look back at his granddaughter to see if she is following him, but Bonisa knows that he can tell by the sound of the twigs breaking under her feet that she is following him.

"My sheep know my voice and they follow me." Again and again it sounds in her heart. "Yes, Inkosi Jesu, I shall follow You."

For hours, Bonisa follows her grandfather along the narrow path, through thick brush and a forest of thorn trees. The path leads slowly upwards to the African highlands. There, Grandfather leaves the forest track and takes another path into an area where elephant grass grows. The grass-stalks are so tall and reach up far above her head. Grandfather is also completely hidden by the tall, thick grass.

In the sun's warm rays, the wind blows through the reedgrass. Bonisa hears the yellow leaves rustle around their stalks. They sing and whisper in the wind as they sway, rocking back and forth. However, it does not scare her now. Oh no, she does not feel as alone now as she did the night they went through the river. She is not alone anymore. She now believes that Inkosi Jesu has come along to this new land. She has heard His voice speaking to her heart: "And they follow me."

She wants to do that now. She may be walking behind Grandfather but she follows Him, who is the Great Shepherd, who will never forsake His sheep.

13. THE 'GREAT MAZENGA'

They have walked the entire day without stopping for rest. Night has already fallen in the woods when they finally arrive at Grandfather's kraal.

A few children are standing at the kraal entrance, talking and looking curiously at the new girl who walks shyly behind Grandfather. Excitedly, they run into the kraal to tell the women that Grandfather is back from his trip to the South.

A busy chattering erupts. The family members come walking toward them. In front is old Ugogo; she walks very slowly, shuffling her feet through the sand. She is hunched over, leaning her right hand on a cane.

Bonisa is shocked as Ugogo comes closer. How old and dirty she looks! She also notices that the women and girls wear only skirts made of animal hides and that they look very different from the people in her own land.

The old grandmother looks sternly at the girl. She examines Bonisa and mutters some baffling words. With her dirty hands, she grabs Bonisa's dress. Her eyes fix on the neck and then on the wrists of the child. She snarls: "Where is your amulet?"

"Ugogo, I don't have an amulet because Inkosi Jesu is my King and I don't pray to the amadhlozi."

The old woman is shocked and lets go of Bonisa's dress. Grandfather speaks with Ugogo for a few moments and then the whole family returns into the kraal. Only Bonisa must wait at the kraal entrance until Ugogo returns from her hut with a new amulet, which contains all the magic power, needed to drive away evil spirits. It is a beautiful necklace made of little black and white beads from the dried bones of wild animals.

Ugogo holds the amulet out in her hands and tells Bonisa that Mazenga, the great medicine man, has put a lot of power in the necklace to get rid of the evil spirits.

Wideeyed, the girl stares at the necklace. As Grandmother is about to hang the amulet around Bonisa's neck, Bonisa steps back and says: "No... you can't do that...! Umfundisi won't allow it."

"Ah... ah, who is this Umfundisi and Inkosi Jesu? We don't know them and they don't live here!" Ugogo exclaims angrily.

"But He is with me and I hear His voice," the child answers.

Again Grandmother tries to put the amulet around Bonisa's neck, and when she refuses again, the old woman becomes furious and snarls that she can't come into the kraal.

With the amulet in her hands, Ugogo shuffles back to the huts where the women are back again at the fires, busily preparing the evening meal.

Among the women, an anxious murmuring starts, about the strange girl who doesn't want to wear an amulet. Oh, she is asking for trouble! She can't live with them. Of course, she has brought evil spirits with her from the land on the other side of the great Shandingu-river. Those spirits will bring sickness and misfortune to the family; those spirits must be chased away immediately!

While Bonisa waits alone by the kraal fence, the entire family talks about what should be done with her. As head of the extended family, Grandfather must make a decision. He sends one of his sons to Mazenga, the witchdoctor, with the request that he would come quickly to drive the evil spirits out of the girl.

In the mean time, two boys in the kraal must beat the drums so that the evil spirits will not dare to escape out of the girl into the kraal.

The last of the golden twilight fades away as the setting sun sinks behind the thick forestcovered hills. Dark clouds drift along the evening sky. In the valley, a herd of black buffalo moves on toward the forest of thorn trees, which will be their shelter for the night. A group of impala frolics blithely, scampering down the hills to go and quench their thirst in the narrow rivers of the valley after a hot day. Rapidly, darkness begins to fall over the forest and with it comes a mysterious silence that announces the arrival of the African night. The kraals, including grandfather's, are enveloped by the still darkness of the night.

Bonisa is sitting on the ground at the entrance of the kraal and leans against the rough wood of the enclosure. She is so tired. Through the gaps of the enclosure, she sees the women and children and a few men sitting by the fires. The evening meal is being handed out.

But she doesn't get any food. She does not belong here; she is the strange girl from Vundla's kraal, far across the great Shandingu-river. The drums are beaten monotonously, on and on. This will ensure that all evil spirits stay outside the enclosure.

Bonisa's head begins to droop and she falls asleep against the rough fence.

"Mazenga is coming," whisper the women. From the dark forest, the great medicine man and his helpers appear. They enter the kraal.

Mazenga disappears into grandfather's hut to discuss which rituals should be performed to free the girl of the evil spirits in order that she may become a new family member.

The flames of the fire rise higher and the flickering light makes the dark shadows dance over the black faces of the men sitting in a big circle on the ground inside the hut.

"Ah..." says grandfather, "this girl is possessed by a strong spirit the spirit of the white people and of their Inkosi Jesu."

"Ah..." answers Mazenga, "my medicines have great power! Am I not the most powerful witchdoctor in the entire Zwabongaland?"

Grandfather keeps silent for some time, then slowly, he says: "Vundla, my daughter MaWanda's husband, has said that all the medicine men of the Shandingu-land couldn't drive away the spirit of that Inkosi Jesu."

The medicine man stares into the fire, enraged. He growls at everyone present in the hut, telling them that his magic power is stronger than that of all the medicine men South of the great river. Mazenga looks impressive of stature as he is seated behind the woodfire. "Bring that girl here!" he commands.

One of the younger women from the kraal must call Bonisa. Her name is Shita. She walks over to the kraal fence, squats beside the sleeping child and awakens her. "Come," she says kindly. "Come along. The great Mazenga is here. He is the priest who was sent by the amadhlozi to convert you into a good, young Zwabonga woman. Come along, and don't be afraid. Let Ugogo put the amulet around your neck so that you will be happy and become part of our tribe."

Bonisa pauses and looks around, still a little drowsy. Of course! She is at Grandfather's kraal.

"Come quickly," Shita urges gently. "Don't let the great Mazenga wait. I will help you."

She takes Bonisa by the hand. The child feels something friendly in Shita's grip. Could there be someone in this kraal willing to help her?

Shita takes her right up to the entrance of the hut and whispers: "Don't be afraid. I will wait for you."

Still slightly scared, Bonisa looks at the dark figures sitting around the fire. In the center sits the 'great Mazenga'. A spotted leopard skin hangs across his chest from his shoulder. Around his neck is a string of monkey-, lion-, leopard-, and wild boar teeth. Two lion claws dangle over his shoulders. On his head is a fur hat of leopard skin from which a few monkey tails swing back and forth. In his right hand he holds a pointed spear. Beside him is his headman with a large, broad shield made of ox hides.

Ugogo shuffles into the hut after Bonisa and lets the child stand right in front of the fire, directly across from Mazenga.

It is quiet in the hut, strangely quiet. Only the crackling of the branches in the fire can be heard.

The great Mazenga looks at the shy girl who stands before him. He looks at her long and hard.

The child folds her hands together and stares into the fire.

Suddenly the medicine man growls. The dull, low sound echoes through the hut. Everyone cringes with fear.

Bonisa presses her hands together more tightly, and prays softly: "Inkosi Jesu, are You still with me?"

Mazenga growls louder and deeper. The sound seems to come from every corner of the hut, and even out of the ground. Like most medicine men, he is a ventriloquist. He begins to shake his head. The monkey tails swing wildly back and forth.

With his left hand he shakes his necklace of wild animal teeth. "Give her the amulet of our Zwabonga tribe," he orders, "so that our amadhlozi will protect her and she will become a good, hardworking Zwabonga woman."

Ugogo shuffles over to the girl to hang the necklace around her neck, and says: "The spirits of our ancestors protect you. From this moment you are a member of our family."

As Ugogo is about to hang the necklace around Bonisa's neck, Bonisa takes a step backward, and in a trembling, childlike voice, she says: "I am not allowed to wear an amulet. Inkosi Jesu is my king; He will protect me."

Still holding the necklace, Ugogo drops her arms again, and looks at Mazenga. The men mutter in shock and the eyes of the great medicine man flare up in anger. An uncomfortable silence takes hold of everyone in the hut.

Bonisa's heart pounds frantically. "Lord, help me," she softly prays. Then, as if from far away, she remembers the voice of old MaRunda at the Mission hospital, when she told Bonisa that Inkosi Jesu said: "If you love me, keep my commandments."

Oh yes, she wants to do that very much; she wants to be obedient to Him.

Mazenga rises to his feet and the other men follow his example. Like ghosts, the shadows of the medicine man and the men dance across the dark-coloured walls of the hut.

The voice of the medicine man rumbles throughout the hut as he demands: "Who is this Inkosi Jesu? Is He mightier than the great Mazenga?"

Bonisa feels so small and afraid; she can barely speak, but she must; she answers: "Inkosi Jesu is the great Son of Jehovah and He is stronger than the great Mazenga."

With burning anger, Mazenga screams: "Take her outside! We will call the amadhlozi for help. Let the drums be beaten loudly so that this evil spirit will be driven away. This child has been bewitched by the white people."

Outside the hut stands Shita. She takes Bonisa's hand and whispers: "Ah, you're a foolish girl! Wear the amulet and everyone will be happy. Otherwise, Mazenga will ask for an offering feast to be made. He will give you medicine that will make you sick. You will be lonely and afraid."

"But I'm not alone. Inkosi Jesu will help me."

"Ah..." says Shita, "but Mazenga is much stronger."

"No," Bonisa answers firmly, "Mazenga is not stronger."

After some time, the medicine man leaves the hut with grandfather and Ugogo. They talk briefly with the other women and men who are sitting outside. There is a sudden commotion throughout the dark kraal.

Bonisa sits on the ground beside Shita's fire while the young woman tells her that she also came from another kraal several years ago, the kraal of a family that was at enmity with Bonisa's Grandfather. Shita also had to be freed from the evil spirits that possessed her. Mazenga came and held an offering feast for her. Fortunately, she was completely cured and married one of Ugogo's sons, a brother of MaWanda, Bonisa's mother.

The child now understands that Shita is her aunt.

Upon Mazenga's command, several women prepare a fire in the hut next to the entrance of the kraal. They put down three stones in between which a fire is made. Over this fire, they put a clay pot filled with water.

The women then carry, several small poles, fastened together into a cone shape, into the hut. Over the top of the poles they hang a few cowhides to form a small tentlike structure.

Mazenga orders Bonisa to follow him into the hut.

"Don't be afraid," Shita assures her.

Bonisa follows the medicine man, wearing his strange priestly garments, inside the hut.

Everyone stares after them in fearful respect as the drums pound their hypnotic sound through the dark night.

Bonisa must sit under the branches covered with cowhides, beside the fire over which the pot of water is now boiling. The 'great Mazenga' sprinkles his magic ingredients into the pot of boiling water. It contains herbs from the forest, tree leaves, finely ground plants, and slivers of tree root. He now asks the ancestors spirits of the Zwabonga tribe to drive away the evil spirits that live inside the girl.

Ugogo makes the fire burn a little more, adds some extra dry branches and soon the red flames lick around the clay pot and the water with the herbs begins to boil faster. There is no lid on the pot and the hot steam of the boiling water rises upward and the small shelter underneath the cowhides fills with hot, steamy air.

Soon, Bonisa begins to wheeze and cough as she inhales the herbal vapor from the pot. Mazenga has sealed the tent tightly so that no vapor can escape.

Bonisa rests her head in her hands. She tries not to breathe in the terrible, burning fumes. Soon, there is hardly any fresh air left in the small tent. Oh, she must breathe, but that strong vapor stings her eyes, and burns inside her nose and down her throat. Bonisa begins to get such a tight feeling in her chest. Outside, the drums beat faster and faster; the sound reverberates through her head.

The pot continues to boil and steam. Bonisa feels increasingly nauseous. Oh, she is sure that she will die! She wants to escape, but that's not possible with Mazenga standing outside in front of the tent.

She starts to cry, and in her anguish she calls: "Inkosi Jesu, do You still see me...? Are You still with me...?"

Her head begins to feel dizzy. It is as if she is being swung back and forth, and then suddenly, she is no longer aware of anything around her. Several minutes later, Ugogo peers in through the small opening of the tent and sees the girl lying motionless on the ground.

Mazenga is called forward, and he speaks: "Ah... now all is well; the spirits have come out of her. Ah... now all is well. The calf must now be sacrificed. Quick... quick... before the evil spirits return."

The women take the tent of cowhides and the pot with water out of the hut. And on the ground inside the hut, lies the unconscious girl. Heavy drops of moisture and sweat glisten on her face and over her entire body.

Shita sneaks into the hut and kneels down beside Bonisa. Carefully she wipes the moisture off Bonisa's small head and checks her pulse. She looks at the still child with compassion. Shita knows how horrible this must have been for Bonisa; when she came to live in this kraal, the same thing was done to her. But this child is so young. Tomorrow she will feel somewhat better and Shita will try to take good care of this girl. Now she fans the sweating body and holds on to the clammy hands of the child.

Mazenga, the medicine man, is seated in the middle of the kraal next to the big woodfire. Grandfather and several other men form a circle around the fire.

A heavy silence hangs over the kraal. The tamtams are quiet; not a sound is heard. Nobody moves until Kwebu, the husband of Shita, enters the kraal with a calf that he had taken from the night kraal at Mazenga's command. Only the snorting of the young animal breaks the silence.

In front of the hut, where Bonisa is lying on the ground, Kwebu stands still. Upon a barely noticeable cue from Mazenga, the boys let the tips of their fingers tap softly on the tightly stretched animal hides of the drums. A soft hum fills the air.

The 'great Mazenga' stares silently into the flames. The great witchdoctor must now coax the good spirits of the Zwabonga ancestors to enter the girl's body; these spirits will give her new life and growth, which will allow her to become a strong, healthy Zwabonga woman. There is power in the blood of a young cow and that is why it must be sacrificed at this time.

The women in the kraal, working under Ugogo's supervision, are now busy filling calabash shells with beer and carry these to the men sitting around the fire.

After everyone has taken a good swallow of beer, Mazenga waves his hands up and down. This signals to the boys to beat the drums even louder.

The night pulsates with the fierce rhythm of the drums. The women and girls form a circle around the calf and their dancing begins. At first slowly and solemnly, then faster and faster they swing and jump around the restless animal, stirred up by the rhythm of the drums.

The glowing fire casts the whimsical shadows of the people on the walls of the huts and among the trees; their screams echo throughout the woods in an attempt to call up the spirits of their ancestors. The dark silhouettes of others from surrounding kraals sneak in to join the offering feast. The women and girls join the others in the circle around the calf. The men are squatting by the fire.

Finally, the 'Great Mazenga' begins to move. His eyes focus on

Kwebu and the young animal. With his hand he reaches inside his pouch and withdraws a long, sharp knife. The men around the fire rise to their feet and the 'great Mazenga' gets up and walks slowly toward the animal that is to be offered.

Quickly and quietly, the women step back and the men and boys form a new circle around the calf that has been brought in front of Bonisa's hut.

While a few men hold tightly onto the young animal, Mazenga drives with a firm hand his sharp knife into the animal's throat; it collapses, bleeding, in front of the hut.

Ah... now all is well! The blood flows over the ground and soaks into the earth; the blood stands for new life and growth.

A new dance begins around the lifeless calf with much shouting and singing. Large gourds with beer are carried in. The beer is drunk by men and women, boys and girls, while the drums are beaten with a breathtaking tempo so that the sound rumbles like thunder through the dark woods. The ancestral spirits will be awakened by this beating and come to the kraal to bring their blessings.

At long last, the first morning light breaks through the dark forest. Drunk and tired of dancing and screaming, the people drag themselves to their huts in exhaustion; they sleep until the sun is beaming high in the sky.

Shita remained in Bonisa's hut, waiting patiently beside the still child. Old Ugogo had been in the hut for a moment to hang the amulet around the girl's neck. Ugogo believes that everything is safe now for Bonisa and for the family with whom she will live. The strange, evil spirits from the land that lies on the other side of the great river, have been driven out of her. A healthy calf was offered to the amadhlozi and the power from its blood had penetrated into her hut. That power must go into Bonisa and give her new life. She now wears the amulet with the power of the

Zwabonga ancestors around her neck so no one has to be afraid anymore. The new girl now belongs completely to the tribe of the Zwabonga people.

Ugogo hobbles to her hut to lie down and immediately falls into a deep sleep, drunk from the beer and exhausted from the calling up of the spirits.

Restlessly, Bonisa tosses and turns her head. Her hands run over the thin hide that covers her body. She moans softly.

Shita, who had lain down beside her to doze a little, sits up straight and looks at the girl.

Bonisa opens her eyes, looks around the hut in bewilderment and shuts her eyes again. For a while she lies very still. Then she opens her eyes again and looks long and hard at Shita.

"Ah..." Shita says, "You're alive again."

The child groans, turns her head, and whispers in a barely audible voice: "Inkosi Jesu."

Shita is shocked; did she hear it right? Whose name did the child speak? She stares anxiously at Bonisa, listening sharply to hear if she will say it again. "You now belong to us," Shita says nervously. "A calf has been offered for you. You have been freed of all the spirits from the land of Vundla. You will now become a true Zwabonga woman."

Bonisa looks at her with big, sad eyes and says softly: "I belong to Inkosi Jesu." Tears well up in her eyes and she begins to cry.

Dismayed, Shita grabs Bonisa's hands tightly and calls: "No... no... that's not possible! You belong to us! Kwebu gave up the most beautiful calf for you. Mazenga sacrificed it. The blood of the offered animal flowed over the ground to give you new life. Now you belong to us... completely!"

Dark, sad eyes focus on Shita's concerned face, and then, Shita notices that there is a wonderful ring in Bonisa's weak voice, as she whispers: " Inkosi Jesu died for me. His blood alone can give me new life." Then she closes her eyes and falls into a deep sleep.

It takes several weeks before Bonisa's strength completely returns. For most part of the day she is in Shita's hut. There she weaves sleeping mats and twists rope from the fiber of tree bark. She is obedient, and willing to do all the work that Shita tells her. Only occasionally does she go outside of the kraal into the forest to gather wood for the fire.

Shita takes care that Bonisa does not come into contact with the rest of the family in the kraal while after Mazenga's feast. Shita is afraid that the girl will talk to them again about the King from the holy book of Umfundisi.

And if Mazenga hears that the spirit of Inkosi Jesu has not been driven out of her, what will happen then? Shita fears the worst. Mazenga will not tolerate any other power than his own in the land of the Zwabongas.

Bonisa soon becomes strong enough to carry heavy loads of wood on her head. Shita also takes her out to the stream to fill gourds with water and carry them back to the kraal. The companionship and help of Bonisa bring a pleasant change into Shita's hard life. She becomes more and more attached to the girl. She also begins to listen with great interest when Bonisa talks about the Lupanda hospital and about Umfundisi and the Holy Book of the Lord Jehovah.

Shita is impressed by Bonisa's firm desire not to wear an amulet because of her trust in the protection of Inkosi Jesu. Bonisa does not need the protection of ancestral spirits.

Shita begins to doubt the almighty power of Mazenga. If even the offering of their most beautiful calf, the vapor ritual with the magic herbs, and the power of the 'great Mazenga' cannot drive the spirit of Inkosi Jesu out of Bonisa, then He must surely be a powerful King. He must be more powerful than the amadhlozi and the 'great Mazenga'.

The evenings that Shita and her husband spend sitting in their hut by the woodfire, are the nicest hours of the day. At first warily

Bonisa has returned from the land of Zwabonga. She asks the people at the Lupanda Mission Post, if someone could go to the other side of the great Shandingu river. The people who live there must also hear the Gospel of the Lord Jesus. That's Bonisa's greatest desire and prayer.

Not long thereafter, the Great Shepherd sends a Missionary from Lupanda to Zwabonga-land; to the people who still live in darkness.

In obedience to his Master's command, he bears witness of the Light, there also. The Good News is made known and medical assistance is given. God's promise is fulfilled: *"The people that walk in darkness have seen a great Light; they that dwell in the land of the shadow of death, upon them hath the light shined."* Isaiah 9:2

"Then Jesus spoke again unto them, saying: 'I am the Light of the World; he that followeth Me shall not walk in darkness, but shall have the Light of Life'." John 8:12

but later boldly, Shita tells her husband everything she has heard from Bonisa. Kwebu does not become angry. He listens closely but warns Shita not to say any of this to Grandfather Dodo.

A plan begins to take shape in Kwebu's mind. He wants to leave the land of the Zwabongas and travel South through the great Shandingu-river to the land of the Lupanda hills. Kwebu has heard from his father Dodo that South of the Lupanda hills one can find work in the mines. Many Africans go there. There, he will be able to build his own kraal and buy good clothes and good food. Kwebu is a young, motivated African. He does not want to stay in his father's kraal.

But fear of Mazenga casts a dark shadow over his plan because no one is allowed to leave the land and nation of the Zwabonga without Mazenga's permission.

While Kwebu prepares his plan to leave Dodo's kraal, Bonisa continues to do her work obediently and willingly. She has helped with the planting and weeding of the corn fields. She has made dye from various kinds of tree roots for Ugogo's reedgrass baskets. She speaks with childlike simplicity about Umfundisi, the Lupanda hospital, the Holy Book and Inkosi Jesu to anyone who wants to hear.

In many kraals, even those far to the North, many hear about the girl in the kraal of Dodo and Ugogo who came from far across the great Shandingu-river. That child has the spirit of Inkosi Jesu inside of her. It is such a powerful spirit that even the magic power of the 'great Mazenga' is not strong enough to drive Him away.

This girl tells that far to the South, beyond the Lupanda valley, lives a white man, a servant of that most powerful medicine man. Umfundisi can help sick people. He can heal blind, sick eyes. He can set free those who have been bewitched and made sick by evil spirits.

And when you go to Umfundisi, you don't have to pay for the

medicine with gifts of cattle or other things. Ah... they have never heard of that before. Every African medicine man asks for payments of cattle or corn.

Umfundisi has been sent to the Lupanda valley by his King to help all the sick. Even people bitten by a poisonous snake can be healed there. The white man reads from the book of Nkulu-Nkulu whose laws and commandments are written there. In this Book is also written that Inkosi Jesu is powerful enough to heal even the very sick.

The women tell each other these things as they fill their gourds at the river. In this unexpected way, people hear about the power of Christ. He is the only Medicine Man for people who are hopeless, helpless and sick; for those in the land of darkness where His Name has not been heard before.

His name is not spoken aloud, oh no! If Mazenga would hear it, he would put to work all his powers to prevent any worship of Inkosi Jesu. Most of the Zwabonga are afraid to talk about Inkosi Jesu because they are only allowed to honour Mazenga. The 'great Mazenga' growls like a wild animal, whenever he hears talk of a medicine man who is more powerful than he.

14. THE VOICE OF THE SHEPHERD

This evening as Shita and Bonisa sit in the hut by the fire, Shita's husband comes to visit. Following behind him into the hut is a skinny boy. They squat next to the fire and for a long time look silently at the glowing embers.

Bonisa notices a strange expression on the skinny boy's face. His head is slightly bowed forward and his hands search over the ground of the hut. She then realizes that his sunken eyes are nearly shut. Oh... now she understands. The boy is blind.

Kwebu looks at Bonisa and asks: "Can the white man heal the eyes of this boy?"

After serious consideration, she answers: "Inkosi Jesu can do it. Umfundisi treated Zenja's eyes when he had fire in his eyes."

"Ah..." says the boy, "I had fire in my eyes. Then they took me to a medicine man and he put drops in my eyes. It was painful, very painful. And then everything went dark. Now it is as though I live in the land where it is always dark."

"Oh... go to Umfundisi. He wants to help you and he won't even ask for payment," Bonisa says excitedly.

The skinny boy smiles happily. But soon the doleful expression on his face returns. His eyes are shut while he says: "The river is wide and the crocodiles are dangerous."

Again, it becomes silent in the hut and the four sit together without saying a word.

Suddenly, Kwebu stands up and carefully closes off the entrance of the hut. Then he whispers: "Listen, I have a plan, but nobody else in the kraal is allowed to know, only you people... because I need all of you to help me."

They listen attentively to Kwebu as he tells them about his intentions. The four of them must try to escape Zwabongaland. Kwebu, with the help of his nephew, has found the shortest route to the river. The rainy season has passed and the water level is so

147

low now that they can easily wade through the river.

Bonisa's heart pounds with excitement. Is she allowed to go with Kwebu? Back to her own land? And is Shita coming along too? She can hardly believe it.

Her happiness is somewhat lessened when Kwebu admits that he fears the power of Mazenga. Oh... if the great medicine man notices that they are leaving the country without his permission, he will be outraged. He will send out his men to track them down. Yet, Kwebu wants to go ahead with his plan.

In three nights, when the moon will cease to give her light, they will set out on their journey.

On the appointed night, the three of them slip silently away. Kwebu walks in front, followed by Shita who carries corn meal, a cooking pot, a sleeping mat and antelope hides for blankets on her head. Bonisa walks behind the others carrying her own belongings on her head. She wears a skirt made of antelope skin and another skin is tied around her shoulders. She cannot wear the yellow dress that was given to her at the Mission Hospital; it is in Shita's basket underneath the corn. People would easily recognize her if they saw her yellow dress.

It is a dark night. Thick clouds race across the midnight sky. They walk quietly and cautiously along the forest path until Kwebu mimics the call of the night swallow. Just a moment later, they hear the same trill coming from the woods.

Blind Kekulu answers the call of the night swallow as a sign that everything is safe. Now they know that everything is going as planned. The blind boy is waiting for them in the woods. He has a goat with him, held by a rope. The animal is coming along on the journey South.

After walking quite a distance, the night wind carries along the smell of fresh, warm beer, and Kekulu picks up the scent of a smoldering fire.

"We are coming up to the kraal," says Kekulu, before the others are able to see the fire. The blind boy is accustomed to sensing things by smell rather than by sight as most people would.

As quietly as possible, they move along the forest path. There is some movement in the bushes next to the path and a deep voice asks them where they are going.

"To see the medicine man," Kwebu answers.

"Ah... to the 'Great Mazenga," the man says, "That's fine," and he disappears among the bushes and into the woods again.

They walk throughout the night and at the first light of dawn they reach the shore of the great Shandingu-river. The crested cranes leave their nightly shelter high up in the trees, their wings flapping noisily over the water. Shita and Bonisa are tired but they are not allowed to rest until they are on the other side of the river.

Kwebu goes down the riverbank first and gauges the depth of the water with a long stick. Fortunately, it is not too deep, although the water nearly reaches Bonisa's shoulders. In this section of the river, there are no stones to step across and the sand sometimes slips away under their feet.

Kekulu must wait on land with the goat until Kwebu has taken his wife and the girl to the other side. After that, Kwebu goes back and carries the goat on his shoulders while Kekulu stumbles through the water beside him.

In the early morning, after a fearful and difficult journey, they are finally standing in the land that Bonisa has longed for so much. The land in which they have the Bible.

Kwebu wants to go on immediately. He is afraid that Mazenga will hear about his escape and send his men after them.

For a moment, Bonisa looks back across the river to the land where she has had so much pain and sorrow.

Suddenly, Kekulu says to her: "Now there is no one in Zwabonga-land who can talk about Inkosi Jesu."

"We will tell Umfundisi," she responds softly.

For two days and two nights, they have been plodding South of the river through the endless, lonely woods. Neither Bonisa nor Kwebu knows the way. Farther and farther East they head, but still there is no sign of the Mission Post.

Occasionally, they stop for a while to rest; Kwebu and Kekulu make a fire on which Shita can roast some corn for them. They drink from the little streams of rainwater before continuing on their journey for several more hours.

Bonisa is exhausted. The stressful events of the past months weigh down heavily on her. There is an intense longing in her heart; a longing for the voice of the Shepherd. The memories of all that she has heard from Umfundisi have begun to fade. She tries not to forget them but it all seems so distant and so long ago. And she cannot hear the voice of Inkosi Jesu in her heart anymore.

Bonisa is sad. She feels weak. She hasn't the strength anymore to look for the Mission hospital. Maybe they will never find the white house. She is feverish and wants to lie down on the forest ground and just stay there. But that's not possible; the wild animals will attack her.

Kwebu is becoming worried that the spirits of the Zwabonga ancestors are angry with him for leaving their land. Maybe that's why Bonisa is sick. Disheartened they drag themselves onward through the lonely woods.

Kwebu carries the ailing girl on his back now; she can no longer walk. Their stubborn goat doesn't want to go on either; Kekulu must keep tugging him forward.

In the twilight of the third day, after having made a wood fire and preparing their last bit of corn, Bonisa becomes very sick. She is delirious and calls for Umfundisi. Shita and Kwebu do not know what to do. Kekulu has become quiet. He is doubtful that they will find the Mission Post, and that his eyes will never be healed.

They are stunned when they suddenly see a man coming toward them. The man greets them and squats next to their fire.

150

He asks from where they have come. He can see that they are afraid and do not want to answer him. Shita lays her arm protectively around Bonisa who lies, moaning, under the antelope skin beside the fire.

The man's voice is friendly and he tells them that he is a teacher at the Mission school in Zendigho. He wants to take them all to his kraal. There they can get food and a good place to sleep for the night.

Along the narrow, rugged path, the tired travellers wind their way through the woods to Reuben's kraal. They are heartily welcomed inside the red clay house of the African teacher. Reuben asks his wife, Mhody, to take good care of their guests and the sick child.

For Shita and Kwebu, such hospitality is unusual. In the land of Zwabonga, strangers from another tribe are never received with such warmth. They notice Reuben has the same friendliness and helpfulness as Bonisa. Timidly, Shita asks Reuben if Inkosi Jesu is also their King, because they take such good care of them.

Surprised and astonished, Reuben stares at Shita. How can this woman, who is dressed in animal hides and who comes from the dark, isolated Zwabongaland, mention the name of the Lord Jesus?

In the corner of the room, Bonisa is laid on the ground. Mhody gently lays a sheet over her to keep off the flies. Bonisa's hands tremble while her head tosses and turns restlessly.

Reuben and Shita stand over the sick child who calls out softly as if she is searching for something she has lost. Her whispered words are barely audible.

Shita kneels down beside the sleeping mat and takes hold of Bonisa's hands. For a moment the girl lies still, opens her eyes, looks at Shita, and says: "I don't hear His voice anymore."

Then she closes her eyes and, again, begins to toss restlessly in her fever.

"Whose voice does she mean?" asks Reuben.

"The voice of the Shepherd," answers Shita.

Reuben stares in amazement at Shita and the sick child.

"Please, tell me who you are!" Reuben asks urgently. "You mention the name of Inkosi Jesu and the child speaks about the voice of the Shepherd. Please, tell me everything."

For Reuben, the African Missionary teacher, this becomes the most wonderful evening he has ever experienced. Deep into the night, he listens to the story of Bonisa told by Shita and Kwebu. He is deeply moved, especially when Shita shares with him that Bonisa, upon reviving from the great Mazenga's vapour ritual, first spoke the name of 'Inkosi Jesu'. From that moment on, Shita's heart had begun to doubt the power of Mazenga.

Through Bonisa's steadfast and childlike faith, they had dared to leave the land of the Zwabonga and had even taken blind Kekulu along with them. Bonisa had heard His voice in her heart: "My sheep know my voice and they follow me." She had always believed but now she is so sad because she can no longer hear the voice of the Shepherd.

There is a long silence.

Bonisa opens her eyes again and looks curiously around the room. Reuben takes the Bible and kneels down beside her. He opens the book and says: "Here is God's Word... Listen to the voice of the Shepherd, who speaks in this Book."

Slowly and clearly, he reads aloud Psalm 23 in their native tongue: "The Lord is my Shepherd."

He then prays for the recovery of the sick child. He also thanks the Great Shepherd for returning this lamb of His flock to the Mission community after having been through so many trials. He prays for the strengthening of her faith so that she will hear the voice of the Shepherd again as she hears the Word of God, the Bible.

After Reuben's prayer, the child looks up at him and weakly reaches for the Bible. The African teacher is moved. He squats down beside her and lays the Bible in her hands.

A smile of peace spreads across her face. Her fingers close around the Holy Book and she softly whispers: "Thank you, Lord." And then, the Bible resting underneath her thin, folded arms, she falls asleep.

Several days later Reuben arrives at the Lupanda hospital with Kekulu. The goat comes along as well, as a gift for Umfundisi. The boy is immediately admitted into the hospital, but the Missionary is unable to bring back light into his sightless eyes.

Zenja, who is now the gardener at the Mission Post, comforts Kekulu and tells him that Umfundisi will speak to him about the Great Light that can shine into dark hearts. Kekulu receives a permanent home at the Lupanda Mission Post and soon becomes a good friend and helper to Zenja.

Reuben spends an entire evening in the hospital and tells Jhula, Amos, MaRunda and the Missionary, the amazing story of Bonisa. All of them thank the Lord for protecting Bonisa and bringing her safely back to her native land. It was God's will for Bonisa to make the long journey to the land of the Zwabonga and live there for several months as a young Missionary to tell about the Lord Jesus. And now, because of her stay in Dodo's kraal, the name of the Great Physician, Jesus Christ, is known in Zwabongaland.

The Missionary agrees to go with Reuben and Amos on the long, arduous journey to the Northland and to establish there, with the help of the Lord, the first Mission Post in that area.

Many weeks pass before Bonisa is strong and healthy again. She stays in the home of Reuben and Mhody. During the day, she goes to the Mission school in Zendigho where Reuben teaches.

A completely new life begins for Bonisa. She receives a good,

Christian education and Reuben promises her that one day she could become a teacher also. Then, she will be able to tell the children of her own tribe about the Great Shepherd who will never let his sheep perish.

But when he saw the multitudes,
He was moved with compassion
on them,
because they fainted,
and were scattered abroad,
AS SHEEP HAVING NO SHEPHERD.

Then saith he unto his disciples,
The harvest truly is plenteous,
but the labourers are few;
Pray ye therefore the Lord of the harvest,
that he will send forth labourers into his harvest.
                              Matthew 9:36-38

Go ye therefore,
and teach ALL NATIONS,
baptizing them
in the name of the Father,
and of the Son,
and of the Holy Ghost;
Teaching them to observe all things
whatsoever I have commanded you.
                              Matthew 28:19

GLOSSARY

Kraal Page 4, Small group of thatched, round huts, where the extended family lives.

Amadhlozi Page 15, Supposed ancestor spirits.

Honey guide Page 106, Latin name - *Indicator variegates*. The bird can guide honey- badgers and man to a bees nest, in order to get its share of the wax and larvae. The bird is can detect the smell of bees' wax, which it eats and is able to digest.

Wild dogs Page 17, Hunting dogs. Latin name: *Lycaon pictus pictus*. These ferocious predators are not domestic dogs, which have gone wild. They are a class of animals very different from dogs. Their habitat is in remote parts of southern Africa.

Nkulu-Nkulu The greatest of all the great ones - God.

Inkosi Jesu The Lord Jesus.

CONTENTS